THE PENG

EDITED

DANTE
THE NEW LIFE

LA VITA NUOVA

TRANSLATED
WITH AN INTRODUCTION BY
WILLIAM ANDERSON

PENGUIN BOOKS

Penguin Books Ltd, Harmondsworth, Middlesex
U.S.A.: Penguin Books Inc., 3300 Clipper Mill Road, Baltimore 11, Md
AUSTRALIA: Penguin Books Pty Ltd, 762 Whitehorse Road,
Mitcham, Victoria

—

First published 1964

—

Translation copyright © William Anderson, 1964

—

Made and printed in Great Britain
by Hazell Watson & Viney Ltd
Aylesbury, Bucks
Set in Monotype Romulus

TO GILLIAN

CONTENTS

INTRODUCTION

A NEW life means a new form of consciousness and this is what Dante described in his first important work. The story related in *The New Life* seems quite simple: Dante as a child met the young Beatrice and fell in love with her. This love continued through various stages of concealment, joy, and open suffering until the death of Beatrice at the age of twenty-four. Bewildered by grief, Dante attempted to seek consolation in the love of another woman, but was recalled to his true love by a vision of Beatrice in glory. However, the mountains of criticism which have arisen around *The New Life* prove that it is not as simple as it seems. There can be little doubt that Beatrice was a real woman and that the events described in *The New Life* are broadly based on fact, but in its pages one finds such an alternation between outward events and inward meanings that it is extremely difficult to disentangle the many threads of thought and experience which went into the writing of the book. Dante stressed the importance of the literal meaning of his works, and *The New Life* should be read first of all for its story. Once the story has been grasped, an attempt can be made to unravel its deeper mysteries. Only by feeling with Dante can one grow to understand why this is one of the most important works in European literature, and one does not immediately appreciate the truth of Jacob Burckhardt's remarks in *Civilization of the Renaissance:*

Even apart from the *Divine Comedy*, Dante would have marked by these youthful poems the boundary between medievalism and modern times. The human spirit had taken a mighty step towards the consciousness of its own secret life.

The figure standing at the centre of this consciousness of the secret life is Beatrice. If one can grasp something of her significance, one is at the beginning not only of an understanding of *The New Life* but also of *The Divine Comedy*. The best statement of the problems surrounding her was made by Dante in the first canzone:

> Love says of her: 'How can a mortal thing
> Have beauty and purity in such wealth?'
> He looks at her swearing to himself:
> 'God meant her as a new creation . . .'

How can a mortal woman like Beatrice be so overflowing in the grace and perfection which are normally considered divine attributes? It is not a problem which can be answered by the cold intellect. Beatrice is beyond the reach of man's ordinary reason, and the more intense emotion produced by reading the poems she inspired is necessary to glimpse her significance. Just as the very title *The New Life* can awaken a memory of a world forgotten since childhood, a world free from the clash of opposing forces and containing infinite prospects of joy, so Beatrice as her influence grows into our minds sometimes appears 'as her followers imagine her'.

Any approach to Beatrice must be made in the light of Dante's times, since by a strange paradox Dante, who was known among his contemporaries for his pride and reserve, made his poetry directly from his own life. This applies no less to *The New Life* than to his later works. Boccaccio tells us in his life of Dante that the first meeting with Beatrice took place at the house of Folco Portinari, Beatrice's father, on May Day 1274. Dante's father had been invited to the celebrations, and he was accompanied by his son, who while playing with other children first set eyes on the young Beatrice. From that moment 'he, child as he still was, received her fair visage into his heart with such affection that from that day forth never, so long as he lived, was he severed therefrom' (Wicksteed's translation). Boccaccio takes pains to stress, as Dante does, that this was a chaste love. Beatrice Portinari was later married to Simone de' Bardi, a member of the Florentine banking family, and she died at the age of twenty-four.

Apart from what Dante tells us, these facts are nearly all that is known of Beatrice. Boccaccio says that to console him for his loss Dante's family married him to Gemma Donati, by whom he had several children. Some critics now think this disproved, saying that Dante was already married by the time of Beatrice's death. His name has been connected with other women also; these include, later in his life, a lovely woman whom for her hardheartedness he christened *La Pietra*, the stony one. At some stage in his youth Dante appears to have led a dissolute life, and he was blamed for this in a sonnet by Guido Cavalcanti, the friend for whom he wrote *The New Life*. Beatrice is, however, totally different in quality from all these other loves: she was his first love and his last. She appears to him when he is still a child, and it is she who welcomes him into Paradise and who remains his connexion with Heaven. She is a creature who can satisfy the dreams of a child, the desire of a passionate young man, and the highest aspirations of a mature artist.

Dante Alighieri was born in Florence in 1265. Although his parents seem to have come down in the world, Dante was able to pursue his studies and to live, at least for much of his youth, a life of leisure. By tradition his family belonged to the Guelph party, which supported the Papacy against the Ghibelline followers of the Emperor, among whom were the greater Florentine aristocracy. Florence at that time was one of the largest cities in Europe; her wealth was based on the textile industry and its related trades and on banking. The total population of about 90,000 was huge for the period. By the end of the thirteenth century Florence had become the bank of the Papacy and had control over the Rome and Naples grain trade. Her representatives were known all over Europe, and the glories of Florence inspired an intense civic consciousness in her people. This pride was shared deeply by Dante, who in *The New Life* always refers to his birthplace as 'the city'. Florence nourished the most extreme contrasts; on the one hand there was the life of the scholars, monks, artists, and poets, the building of the new cathedral, and the encouragement of trade; in contrast to this were the constant quarrels between the nobility and the upper merchant class, violent blood feuds, and the insidious operations of the Inquisition. Dante must have grown up in the atmosphere of monks and artists, but when his outstanding abilities as an orator and diplomat later drew him into public life, he soon learned the extent of bitterness in Florentine politics, since it led to his perpetual exile from the beloved city.

Not much is known about Dante's education, except that he came under the influence of Brunetto Latini, a scholar and writer of international renown. Latini is praised by the Florentine historian Villani for civilizing the Florentines, and in the *Inferno* Dante pays tribute to him as the one who taught him 'how man became eternal'. In his two works, the *Trésor* (which was written in French) and the *Tesoretto*, Latini expounded his theory of rhetoric which greatly influenced the writing of *The New Life*. It has been thought that Dante's education mostly took the form of study of the law in preparation for a public career, though it is difficult to see how a man of his attainments could have been kept to one subject. He studied for a time at Bologna, where the university was not only the great legal centre of Italy but was also famous for its poets. As a result of his wide contacts and education Dante became as much a universal man as any later paragon of the Renaissance; he was not only a poet but a lawyer, politician, administrator, and diplomat, philosopher, theologian, and amateur of the natural sciences, and, what to him included all these activities, a Christian of the thirteenth century searching for salvation. In studying *The New Life* we are mostly concerned with him as a poet, a philosopher, and a Christian.

As a poet Dante was the heir to a well-developed tradition of writing love poetry in the vernacular to an idealized woman. Although poets had used their native tongues in Southern France and Italy long before Dante's birth, he still felt that he needed to justify himself for writing of serious matters in Italian instead of Latin. As it was his intention to raise the treatment of love to a level never before attained, by introducing this higher conception he was trespassing upon the preserves of the Church, whose language was Latin.

The tradition of courtly love had altered greatly from the time when it was first fostered in the south of France. In its beginnings it had assumed the convention of addresses paid by the poet to a woman who was generally in a higher social position than himself and who was also married to another man. Throughout the twelfth century up to the devastation caused in the south of France by the Albigensian crusade, there flourished schools of poets who devised the most intricate forms of rhyme and metre to express adoration of their ladies. The theme of adultery is obvious in the convention, and there always had to be a choice for the poet at some stage in his life between his adulterous love and the salvation promised him by the Church. There was no reconciliation possible between the two philosophies. The tradition came to Italy by means of the Sicilian court of the Emperor Frederick II, who was a poet himself and who gathered other poets around him. Owing to the Moslem influences at this court, the theme of adultery faded away, and the idealized woman did not have to be married to another man before the poets addressed her.

The tradition was continued on the Italian mainland by Guittone d'Arezzo and Rinaldo d'Aquino, but it was not until it reached the understanding of Guido Guinizelli of Bologna that it went through a radical change. The most important feature in his mature work is the inner workings of his love for his lady and not its outward course. It is his poem *Al cor gentil ripara sempre amore* (Love always shelters with the gentle heart) that Dante quotes in his sonnet in *The New Life*, 'Love is the same as a gentle heart,' and he calls Guinizelli *il Saggio*, the wise man. Guinizelli's lady is sent from God and is likened to an angel, but the only satisfaction he can gain from her is the greeting or recognition which was the reward of the earlier Provençal poets.

The next important poet is Guido Cavalcanti, Dante's greatest friend. He was deeply interested in philosophy, and some of his poems, especially the canzone *Donna mi prega*, are abstruse to the point of incomprehensibility. What is most striking about him is his honesty and accuracy. One of his mistresses, Giovanna, appears in *The New Life*, preceding Beatrice as John the Baptist preceded Christ. Like Dante, Cavalcanti addressed his poems to the few who could understand, but where they part company is over their final interpretation of Love. To both of them Love in its truest aspect is only experienced by noble and intelligent men. Dante's Love however leads him back to Heaven, while Cavalcanti's leads him to Death. Death is constantly mentioned in the two friends' works, but for Cavalcanti Love means suffering, which is only rarely redeemed by slight recognition from his lady and which, however much it may be rationalized, never loses its sting.

It is in *The New Life* that we find a complete transformation of this theme of the idealized woman. Death may always be present in Dante's thoughts, but it is always a death which one has to endure to experience a new life. His Beatrice has been sent to earth from Heaven, as were the ladies of Guinizelli and Cavalcanti, but neither of the two older poets says in his poems that he was saved by his lady, as Dante is. Whereas with them the movement was only downwards from Heaven, in *The New Life* Beatrice dies and draws up Dante's highest aspirations to her position, where Mary is, in the heaven of humility. Thus through this chaste love the conflict between the teaching of the church and the worship of the earthly lady is resolved.

The reconciliation which Dante achieved between the troubadour tradition and Christian teaching has many counterparts in the intellectual and artistic movements of the thirteenth century. Scholastic philosophy, the school in which Dante was trained, was intent on reconciling Aristotle's teachings with those of the Church Fathers. Erwin Panofsky has shown, in his *Scholasticism and Gothic Architecture*, that the cathedral-builders worked intellectually in much the same way as the philosophers; to them buildings of the past had the same authority as the Fathers had for the theologians. In solving a problem of construction they did not reject one course in favour of another, but sought to join the two together by means of a third all-inclusive design. Just as the cathedral would be built with this need to reconcile in mind, so a *Summa* would be written with the object of meeting equally the demands of belief and understanding; each argument would have another brought against it, and the points involved would be divided, subdivided, and resolved. The schoolmen had, in fact, a passion for breaking down their works into books, chapters, sections, and subsections, and the most classic example of this is to be found in the *Summa* of St Thomas Aquinas. These theologians strongly influenced the forms of literary writers, so that the urge to clarify and to state clearly the stage of clarification which had been attained became what Panofsky calls 'a mental habit'. This should be borne in mind when the reader comes up against the divisions which follow or precede nearly every poem in *The New Life*. Dante went about the writing of this work intent on stressing its formal cohesion just as much as on relating a story. He states clearly in his prologue what the book is about. He pretends that he is like a scribe writing a scholastic gloss on part of another book, which is in fact the book of his memory. He copies down everything of importance in this book, stating where he considers he is making a digression, and by choosing this form demands the attention of the best minds of his day. Even rhyme was considered as part of the logical scheme of the work.

The divisions which accompany the poems have often come in for criticism, but they are interesting not only because they show the extent of scholastic domination but because they reveal Dante's consciousness as an artist. This consciousness is revealed in these obvious divisions and also in the wider construction of the work. It has always been well known that *The Divine Comedy* is divided into three parts, symbolizing the Trinity, and that it is made up of 100 cantos, of which the first one acts as a prologue, leaving 99 cantos, a number twice containing the number nine, which is connected with Beatrice and which also is divisible by three. In *The New Life* Dante was already indulging his taste for the symbolism of numbers. The three visions foretelling Beatrice's death all contain the number nine. That they are three in number reflects Dante's later reminder that three is the root of nine. There are three main canzoni in the work, the second of which marks the centre of *The New Life* and contains the false vision of Beatrice's death. These canzoni divide the work as a whole into three parts. Charles Singleton points out in his brilliant *Essay on the Vita Nuova* (Harvard University Press, 1949):

By now, the introductions to most editions of the *Vita Nuova* make a point of it, usually seeing the whole design as one to be represented by the figures 10;I; 4-II-4; III; 10 (Roman numerals being the canzoni). But, given the exceptional importance of the number nine in this work, it would seem much more significant to consider the first and last groups of the shorter poems as made up of nine plus one. This would require only that we count the first poem of the *Vita Nuova* as an introductory one, much as we count the first canto of the Inferno; and that we consider the last poem of the book as a kind of epilogue, which, given its nature, it may well be. Such a pattern seems more meaningful for the *Vita Nuova*, in that it can be stated in terms of nine and three and one: 1;9;I;4-II-4;III;9,1. Or more simply, and with perhaps even greater suggestiveness, as 1;9;1;9;1;9;1, since in this way the mysterious number nine is more clearly seen to occur three times.

Thirteenth-century philosophy was dominated by the reintroduction of the works of Aristotle. Dante was familiar not only with his works but also with the commentaries of Albertus Magnus and Aquinas upon them. To Dante, Aristotle was 'the master of those who know', and he is referred to twice in *The New Life*. Dante uses the familiar

Aristotelian terms of substance and accident, potentiality and actuality, in describing the effect of Beatrice's smile and in his digression on the nature of Love, but adapts them very much to his own purposes. For example, when he speaks of Beatrice's smile he says it is so powerful that it can bring forth Love even where it does not exist in potentiality, while in his introduction to the last sonnet he quotes from Aristotle's *Little Metaphysic* to prove a most mystical point of his own. The whole work is particularly interesting for its tension between Neo-Platonism and Aristotelianism. The appearances of Love in the three visions are surely Neo-Platonic in their inspiration and in their mood. Dante undergoes a training in definite stages of the understanding of Love, according to the tradition which goes back to the *Symposium*. Love is portrayed as a god who gains absolute domination over Dante's heart, and he possesses a knowledge of the future which is denied to Dante's mortal mind. His power seems to grow even greater as he replaces one 'disguise' lady by another, dismisses the second one from Dante's mind, and in fact has absolute command right up to his happy appearance at the vision of Beatrice and Giovanna. Then there comes a sudden change; Dante destroys this Platonic conception of Love as a god by applying Aristotelian terms to him and calling him an accident of a substance. This comes as a shock, since up to that point Love has possessed almost more character than Beatrice herself; but it is a necessary stage, since at the end of the fourteenth sonnet Love, by pointing out Beatrice's resemblance to himself, resigns all his rights to her. It is after this that Beatrice appears to people as an angel, as a living witness of a miracle. Just as Love gets rid of the second 'disguise' lady because she has become an impediment to Dante's development, so Dante has to dismiss Love, by reducing him to his proper proportions, so that he can devote himself entirely to Beatrice. From this point onwards Love is no longer a sure guide. After the death of Beatrice he prompts the mistaken attachment to the lady of the window, and the vision of Beatrice is needed to drive out the false love. The final sonnet seems to reconcile the two philosophical positions, when Dante uses Aristotle to explain why his rational mind cannot understand the Platonic mysteries which his sigh describes to him.

Dante's knowledge of Platonic ideas would have come to him in a large part from Boethius. In the *Convivio*, the unfinished work on philosophy which Dante wrote later in life, he states that to console himself for his misery after Beatrice's death he took refuge with the Lady Philosophy, and he mentions the two books which gave him the most help. One was Boethius's *The Consolation of Philosophy* and the other Cicero's *De Amicitia*. It was obviously the first of these which meant the most to Dante, for it supplied him with the idea of interweaving prose passages with poems in which the matter of the prose was concentrated. Boethius's book, written in A.D. 524, was one of the most influential to survive the Dark Ages into medieval times. Boethius had been unjustly imprisoned, and had reconciled himself to his approaching death by writing down everything of value he had learned in his days of good fortune. As he was a paragon of learning, and had devoted his leisure to a study of the works of Plato and Aristotle in an effort to reconcile their apparent and obvious differences, his work is packed with the ideas of the ancient world. Dante owed much to Boethius, and celebrates him in the *Paradiso*. There are many interesting parallels between *The Consolation of Philosophy* and *The New Life* apart from their similarity of structure. *The Consolation of Philosophy* begins with a

19

poem which has been dictated to Boethius by the false muses; this poem does no more than express his self-pity. However, Boethius is suddenly faced with a majestic vision of Philosophy who upbraids him for his fickleness in forgetting her. She remains with him until she has restored all his powers of reasoning and has brought back to his memory all that she ever taught him. Dante gives way to self-pity also when he writes poems lamenting what he considers Beatrice's unkindness to him. He is equally upbraided by the ladies in *The New Life* for his self-pity, and he goes away covered in shame to write his first great poem, *Ladies whose understanding is of Love*. Memory is also a connecting link between the two writers, since Philosophy is concerned first of all with bringing back Boethius to spiritual health by making him remember, and Dante writes copying out everything of importance he finds in the book of his memory. Boethius is taken on a mental journey of return, so that he can understand from a level beyond the stars whence his soul had its origin. Dante's final sonnet tells of the ascent of a sigh to the Empyrean, beyond the region of the fixed stars, where it can gaze upon Beatrice in glory, and he cannot understand the sigh's description of heaven until it makes him remember Beatrice: 'And then, dear ladies, I can understand.'

Dante considered that any work which demanded serious thought and treatment should contain four levels of meaning. These he enumerated in the *Convivio* as the literal, the allegorical, the moral, and the anagogic. The first sense is the literal, and in that sense all the others are included. Dante says that it would be impossible and irrational to comprehend the other senses without the literal meaning. The allegorical sense means the truth hidden under a beautiful fiction, as Orpheus charming the wild beasts is a fiction hiding the truth that a wise man by the use of words can subdue and humble cruel hearts. The third sense is moral, and Dante illustrates this by saying that when Christ ascended the Mount for the Transfiguration he took with him three apostles only out of the twelve, and this can be understood in the moral sense that in the most secret affairs we should have few companions. The fourth and last sense, the anagogic, is spiritual understanding, which is beyond the senses. This is particularly interesting when applied to *The New Life*, for when Dante enters the presence of Beatrice, we are told that Love destroys his spirits of perception, thus pointing to the highest level on which Beatrice has to be understood.

Beatrice is often accompanied by symbols, numbers, and analogies, and the most strongly hinted of these is her Christ-like nature. In the dream in the second canzone foretelling her death, the earthquake, the darkening of the heavens, and other portents are plainly meant to refer the reader's mind to the events which accompanied the Crucifixion. In Beatrice's appearance following the canzone, Giovanna acts the part of John the Baptist, and the very words of the Baptist are applied to Beatrice. Terms of grace and salvation accompany descriptions of her presence, and after the vision of Beatrice which dispels his love for the lady of the window, Dante watches the pilgrims travelling to Rome to see the Veronica, the true image of Christ's face.

To a large extent we have lost the faculty of seeing that an idea or image can be true on several levels at once. However, medieval man seems to have had little difficulty in understanding this, and many mystics encouraged the development of the powers of analogy as a necessary stage in spiritual growth. Dionysus the Areopagite, for example, justifies the use of the basest images in the following way:

21

Thus all those who are wise in Divine matters, and are inter-
preters of the mystical revelations, set apart in purity the Holy
of Holies from the uninitiated and unpurified, and prefer
incongruous symbols for holy things, so that Divine things
may not be easily accessible to the unworthy, nor may those
who earnestly contemplate the Divine symbols dwell upon the
forms themselves as the final truth. Therefore we may celebrate
the Divine Natures through the truest negations and also by
the images of the lowest things in contrast with Their own
likeness.

The faculty for understanding several things at once, upon
which such images depended, had been lost by the time *The
New Life* was first printed in the sixteenth century. It was
no blasphemy to Dante's contemporaries that Beatrice
should be identified on the highest level with Christ and his
Love in a writing whose basis was the literal and true story
of the poet's love and lament for a dead woman called
Beatrice. However, before the work was printed in 1576
the Inquisition ordered several expressions, which it
thought should be reserved for the Godhead alone and
which Dante had applied to Beatrice, to be altered to less
sanctified epithets.

The precision which Dante achieved in his poems, the
structure of his works and his philosophy, is also evident in
the religious background of the work. We have not only lost
the faculty of grasping meaning on many levels; we have
also lost the sense of a clearly defined cosmology related to
religious belief. Although the structure of the nine moving
heavens, which derived from Ptolemy, was not part of the
dogma of the Church, it was universally accepted that all
the angelic orders were assigned their places in a planetary
system according to their level of virtue. Thus when Dante
described the passing of Beatrice up into heaven it was not

merely a vague afterworld which he meant but a clearly
defined position in the Empyrean, the heaven of humility,
where her especial virtues had drawn her. At the beginning
of *The New Life* Beatrice's birth is connected with the
heaven of the fixed stars, whose virtues are Faith, Love, and
Charity. We are also told that at her birth the nine heavens
were in their most perfect conjunction. Then, when she
dies, she has so far outsoared the promise of her birth
that she returns to the highest possible level of all, the
Empyrean. Thus it is not only Dante's spiritual life
which develops during *The New Life*, but Beatrice also
attains a more glorious state, in the Sempiternal Rose,
surrounded by

the first Order of Celestial Beings which are established about
God, immediately encircling Him: and in perpetual purity they
encompass his Eternal Knowledge in that most high and
eternal Angelic dance, rapt in the bliss of manifold blessed con-
templation, and irradiated with pure and primal splendours.
(Dionysus the Areopagite: *The Celestial Hierarchies*).

Another strong religious influence of the time is that of
the Spiritual Franciscans. These were followers of the Cala-
brian abbot Joachim da Fiore, whose interpretation of history
as the three ages of the Father, the Son, and the Holy
Ghost was widely spread. The age of the Son began with the
life of Christ, and the age of the Holy Ghost promised the
disappearance of the earthly Church and its temporal power,
the coming of an age of peace and freedom and a new revelation of Divine Love. These beliefs, which were bitterly con-
tested by many members of the Church, since they obviously
struck at the Papacy and the temporal wealth of its followers,
were current among people of all classes, who viewed with
detestation the gradual degradation of the Church throughout the thirteenth century. Some have even claimed that

The New Life is a cryptic manifesto of the Spirituals, and that Beatrice represents the sacramental graces of the Church of the Age of the Son. Her death, according to this idea, symbolizes the withdrawing of the power of the sacraments from the world and the start of the Age of the Holy Ghost. This in my view distorts the individual, personal, and interior qualities of *The New Life*, and is not supported by the relationship between Dante and Beatrice on the important literal level.

However, one cannot overestimate the importance of the influence of the Franciscans on Dante. The devotion to the Lady Poverty which the Spirituals insisted upon, in contrast to the more lax followers of their founder, must have seemed all the more striking to the young Dante in the midst of the rich and money-grubbing Florentines. Even if he did not, as some have suggested, become a novice at the Franciscan church of Santa Croce for a time in his youth, he must certainly have heard the Spiritual leaders preach at that church. The apocalyptic note which runs throughout *The New Life*, the foreboding note of a coming change, the promise of a new understanding, very probably owe much to the influence of these devoted and extreme ascetics. It seems more likely, if one takes into account Dante's ability to use any idea, whether it be Platonic, Franciscan, or Moslem, and to synthesize it in his own poetry, that he did the same with the ideas of Joachim da Fiore. He in fact made the ideas personal; his love for Beatrice before her death can be compared to the state of the Church in the closing phases of the Age of the Son. Beatrice at this stage can be seen and her actions have a miraculous effect, just as the Church was visible and her sacraments had their power. When Beatrice dies, and her direct miraculous effect can no longer be felt, it is as though the ability to celebrate mass had deserted every priest of the Church. Dante is lost, and wanders in his misery into his unfruitful encounter with the lady of the window. He is recalled from this by the vision of Beatrice in glory, and this might be compared to the first signs of the coming Age of the Holy Ghost. It is possible that Dante took these vast apocalyptic ideas, with their immense exterior range, and turned them into an interior and private account of the growth of his understanding of Love. A parallel, though not such a deep one, might be Donne's use of the new political language of his time in his imagery of courts, princes, and power to express the private psychology of his love poems.

An even more unexpected influence is that of the Moslem world of art and philosophy. In the thirteenth century there was a growing respect for the intellectual superiority of Moslem civilization. It was through Moslem scholars that Aristotle was restored to the west. Their philosophers such as Averrhoes had a wide-ranging influence upon the scholastic philosophers, and their abilities as astronomers and mathematicians showed clearly that western thinkers were far behind their infidel counterparts. The tradition of courtly love which Dante inherited had long before his birth been transformed by the strong Moslem influences at the court of the Emperor Frederick II in Sicily. Dominican and Franciscan friars who had hopes of converting the Moslem world earnestly studied all they could obtain of the Moslem works of religion and philosophy. The nearest source of this culture to Italy was Spain, and Dante probably gained his familiarity with Moslem thought from Brunetto Latini, his master, who was the Florentine Ambassador to the court of Alphonso the Wise in 1260. The court of this king acted as a meeting-place for the two civilizations. Professor Miguel Asín y Palacios, who first pointed out the remarkable

familiarity Dante possessed with the Moslem world, gives
two particularly fascinating instances of the effect of this
culture on *The New Life*. The first of these is the parallel
between the second vision of Love, in which the god appears as a young man, and a *hadith* attributed to the ninth-
century traditionist, Tabrani, which tells of a vision
experienced by Mohammed, in which God appeared 'as a
beardless youth of great beauty'. Of even greater interest
are the many parallels he draws between two books of Ibn
Arabi, a Spanish Moslem poet of Murcia, and the *Convivio*.
Even the extraordinary new conception of Love seems to
derive from the intense romanticism of some of the Sufi
poets, especially Ibn Arabi. There is no other known source
in European literature for this revolutionizing idea of sexual
love sublimated into the means of salvation itself, and when
we know that Ibn Arabi asserted that it is God who appears
to every lover in the image of his beloved, we may be nearer
to understanding how Dante was able to stress the Christ-
like nature of Beatrice.

In mentioning all these varied instances, I have intended
only to point to the immense comprehension and power of
Dante's mind. His own thirst for knowledge and enlighten-
ment forced him to spy out the possibilities of every idea and
belief that came into his consciousness. Probably what
preserved him from ever being captured for long by any one
theory was what Jacques Maritain has called his creative
innocence. Maritain, in *Creative Intuition in Art and Poetry*,
speaks of Dante's 'blessed naïvety', which makes him believe
his love for Beatrice 'to be in itself and in the face of all men
as important a thing as heaven and earth'. Dante in *The
New Life* may be miserable, bewildered, or in the depths of
shame, but never so much that the original fount of his
poetry is sullied. His delight in creating is in itself enough

to take *The New Life* far beyond the apparent level of
death, loss, and misery in the story. Few poets have ever
been able to communicate their own pleasure in writing as
Dante does when he relates the occasion of the first canzone,
when, as he wandered beside a stream of water, the symbol
of living truth, his tongue as if moved by itself spoke the
words 'Ladies whose understanding is of Love'. Any man
who has a creative power within him as strong as that has a
strength to withstand and transform to his own uses any
cultural influence, however fresh and exciting. One can say
that the strength of this creative innocence lay in the fact
that he never lacked the emotion needed to understand, and
then to transform, any idea which attracted him. Throughout his career he nursed and cultivated this purity of heart,
enabling him to synthesize the ideas of many cultures and
so indeed make his own new life.

He was keenly aware that his strength lay here. When, in
the twenty-fourth canto of the *Purgatorio*, he tells of his
meeting with an older Italian poet, Bonagiunta da Lucca, he
is asked whether it was he who wrote the new rhymes
beginning 'Ladies whose understanding is of Love'. Dante
replies 'I am one who, when Love inspires me, listens and
writes down according to the style he dictates within me.'
Thus to him his inspiration is as private and as interior as
the voice of conscience, and this should be borne in mind
when the reader comes to question some of the many apparent illogicalities in *The New Life*. For this is the real crux
in all Dante studies: on the one hand it is obvious that
Dante was one of the most universally conscious and deli-
berate of all poets who have ever written, and on the other
hand his works seem to abound in inconsistencies and open
self-contradiction. If one realizes the fullness of the first
statement, it becomes very difficult to substantiate the

charges of the second without being hurled back upon the rock of one's own unagile thoughts. But some of these problems must be mentioned. Was Dante's attachment to the two 'disguise' ladies deeper than he later wanted to admit? Why in *The New Life* does he imply that this love for the lady of the window lasts only a few days, when it is obvious from the *Convivio* that it was a few years? Why does he devote so much of the *Convivio*, which he wrote much later, to this lady of the window, when he says in *The New Life* that all thoughts of her were expelled by the vision of Beatrice? The way in which some scholars have put these doubts makes Dante into a monster of disingenuousness, which we know he was not.

The best way of approaching these difficulties is from the standpoint of the two visions of Beatrice in glory with which the work closes. It was these visions that led to the writing of the book, and two such visions could not help altering the book of memory from which Dante copied out his experiences. *The New Life* was written at the latest in 1295, when Dante was thirty, five years after Beatrice's death. It is known that Dante wrote love poems to other women apart from Beatrice and the lady of the window, and Beatrice can rarely have been in his mind at the time of writing them. But if one recalls the effect that these visions would have had on his memory and that Dante is recording the stages in his understanding of love, it is not surprising that these minor affairs should be treated as disguises to his real love. Dante at those stages is entirely in the hands of Love. The god in his first two appearances stresses Dante's ignorance of where he is heading and the significance of what he is doing. Afterwards, however, when Dante looked back on the events he was about to chronicle, he must have seen these affairs as necessary stages in his approach towards

Beatrice; they were 'disguise' ladies nearly as much to himself as to the outer world. The prose passages were written after the events had happened, while the poems were the immediate results of the events. When he wrote the great second canzone he did not know that the death of Beatrice which was prophesied in the vision would come so soon upon him; all the events immediately after his recovery pointed to an increased earthly enjoyment of the sight of her. It was when he was starting his strongest admission of his domination by Love that he heard the news of her death. The significance of that poem at the time of its writing was totally different from its significance after the visions of Beatrice in glory had opened the book of memory. These final visions probably entirely changed Dante's attitude not only to the lady of the window but also to all the events which had preceded that episode. To take one of his own favourite images, Dante is like a pilgrim who has an inspiration to seek a certain shrine. On his journey there he visits other shrines, and is sometimes tempted to think that each one of these is the shrine meant by his first vision, but he stays at none of them for long. When he finally reaches the real shrine and looks back on his journey, he can see that the others at which he gained some understanding were necessary stages of his journey, and that if he had not visited these as well he would never have come to the end of his travelling.

Returning now to the threefold structure of *The New Life,* it can be considered from the standpoint of Dante's development in the understanding of Love. The first stage lasts up to the writing of the first canzone, dealing with the first meeting with Beatrice, the two 'disguise' ladies, the denial of the greeting, and the mocking episode; it shows Dante in love, but self-centredly in love. It is only when he meets the ladies who ask him why he dares to say that his blessedness lies in praising his lady, when he has written several poems of complaint, that he is ready not only for the second stage of love but also to write poems. The second stage lasts to the death of Beatrice, and shows the progress he made in this new understanding. However, he is scarcely prepared for the shock of her death, which opens the third stage of the book. In his grief Dante fell into an infatuation with the lady of the window, and this step he obviously, at the time of writing *The New Life*, regarded as a retrogression. He had been granted a love almost more glorious in its effects and promise than he could convey, and when Death appeared to deprive him of it he was too weak to understand that it was a death necessary to a new life. Thus he tried to make this lady into a substitute for Beatrice, who could in fact never be replaced. The lady of the window becomes in the violence of his reaction an enemy of reason, and this seems strange if we compare this passage with the *Convivio*, where she is transformed into an allegory of Philosophy. At the end of *The New Life* Dante states that he studies as hard as he can, to be able to write of Beatrice what has never before been said of any woman, and in the *Convivio* he tells in a moving passage the agony cost him by his search for truth in Philosophy. According to most critics this lady is a very real woman, and his infatuation with her coincided with this long period of study. When Beatrice appeared to him in glory, she did not so much destroy this love or this desire for study as reduce both to their proper scale. For if one considers the fourth level of meaning, the anagogic, a level which is beyond the normal reach of reason, Dante could neither study properly nor preserve his detachment towards this lady, because he had forgotten Beatrice, the revelation beyond reason which is necessary to balanced reason. To write *The Divine Comedy*, Dante was forced to study, but he could only write it if he also remembered Beatrice. In his desire to know he had forgotten the purpose of knowing.

Much of what I have said, in leading up to discussing Beatrice herself, is included in this perceptive passage in Shelley's *Defence of Poetry*:

The freedom of women produced the poetry of sexual love. Love became a religion, the idols of whose worship were ever present. It was as if the statues of Apollo and the Muses had been endowed with life and motion, and had walked forth among their worshippers; so that earth became peopled by the inhabitants of a diviner world. The familiar appearance and proceedings of life became wonderful and heavenly, and a paradise was created as out of the wrecks of Eden. And as this creation itself is poetry, so its creators were poets; and language was the instrument of their art: *'Galeotto fu il libro, e chi lo scrisse.'* The Provençal Trouveurs, or inventors, preceded Petrarch, whose verses are as spells which unseal the inmost enchanted fountains of the delight which is in the grief of love. It is impossible to feel them without becoming a portion of that beauty which we contemplate: it were superfluous to explain how the gentleness and elevation of mind connected with these sacred emotions can render men more amiable, more generous and wise, and lift them out of the dull vapours of the little world of self. Dante understood the secret things of Love even more than Petrarch. His *Vita Nuova* is an inexhaustible fountain of purity of sentiment and language; it is the idealized history of that period, and those intervals of his life which were dedicated to love. His apotheosis of Beatrice in Paradise, and the gradations of his own love and her loveliness, by which as by steps he feigns himself to have ascended to the throne of the Supreme Cause, is the most glorious imagination of modern poetry.

All the theories, all the philosophies, all the religious influences would have remained separate and unfused in

Dante's mind, had he never set eyes on Beatrice. To have inspired such a love she must have been of the most noble and saintlike character. Every one has his own image of her beauty and her charm, but it is almost impossible to sound the depths of her soul. In *The New Life* Dante had to be content to describe the effects of her presence and her being. He had to wait nearly to the end of his life before he was capable of depicting her character. Her enrapturing smile, which dissolves veil after veil of ignorance, her wit, her trust, and mercy, as they appear in the *Purgatorio* and the *Paradiso*, are enough to make Dante the most enviable of all lovers and to explain the audacity of what he says of her death in *The New Life*. To go straight to heaven after death is the prerogative of a saint, and this is what Dante says Beatrice's soul did. For her there was no period in purgatory, because there were no sins for her to purge. God Himself calls her to join His blessed. The daring of this can only be explained by the fact that Dante earnestly believed her to have attained the level of sainthood and that her life was the expression of God's wish to manifest a new miracle upon earth. All attempts to explain her as an allegory or a symbol of virtues merely degrade her, for no virtue can be more wonderful to us than in its appearance and actions in a human soul. Italy in the thirteenth century possessed an extraordinary multitude of holy people who were considered in their own lifetime to have attained sainthood, and when Dante, through the greater understanding and consciousness bestowed upon him by his love, was able to recognize the heights of charity which Beatrice reached in her short life, he performed his own act of canonization.

'There is none like her, none.' One of the most astounding things about *The New Life* is that it contains not a hint of the tradition of love poetry dwelling upon the decay of beauty and the depredations of Time. This tradition, running from Catullus through Ausonius to the medieval Latin lyricists, gains its power by stressing that beauty grows ugly, that time destroys love, and that the rose will fade. Beatrice in contrast to this is as eternally young as the Sempiternal Rose, in whose petals she has her home, is eternally in perfect bloom. She has become independent of mortal time, and when she appears to Dante in the first vision after her death it is as she was at their first meeting. Just as Love says in one of the visions that he is as the centre of a circle from which all parts of the circumference are equally distant, meaning that he can see all parts of time, past, present, and future, so Beatrice has gone to the *nuovo secol*, the new cycle of time to which all history is equally present. At certain times in the *Paradiso* Dante speaks of the presences of some spirits as their lives, as though their holiness had transformed every impression of their earthly existence to such a point that the whole of their lives were present with them in Heaven. In her new life Beatrice has been granted everything of her earthly existence, and in recalling her life Dante adds something of the ecstasy and intenseness of her re-created feelings to his own verse. The visions in which Love appears are later dismissed as allegories, but no such destructive logic is applied to the two visions of Beatrice in glory. These were as real to Dante as the appearances of Christ on earth after the Crucifixion, and after the last of them we can definitely see the fixed intention in his mind to write the great work which developed into *The Divine Comedy*.

At the end of the *Paradise* Dante was able to express his conception of the Love which fills and guides the Universe. Many years of study and growth of feeling had to pass after *The New Life* before Dante could write the last cantos of St Bernard's hymn to the Virgin. However, what we do see in the earlier work is his first dedication of his life to his poetry, his joy in discovering a higher form of creation, the song of degrees in his ascent towards divine Love, and the marking of a new stage in man's consciousness of himself as an individual. There is a remarkable passage in Book XIII of St Augustine's *Confessions* which tells of the same journey and the same truths that Dante was expressing in *The New Life*. St Augustine is speaking here of the gift of the Holy Spirit, the Pentecostal fire, but if one relates the passages to the development of both Beatrice and Dante little more needs to be said:

It is in your Gift that we find our rest. It is in him that we enjoy you. The place where we find rest is the rightful one for us. To it we are raised by love. To it your Spirit lifts us up, lowly creatures as we are, *from the gate of death*. It is in goodness of will that we find our peace.

A body inclines by its own weight towards the place that is fitting for it. Weight does not always tend towards the lowest place, but the one which suits it best, for though a stone falls, flame rises. Each thing acts according to its weight, finding its right level. If oil is poured into water, it rises to the surface, but if water is poured on to oil, it sinks below the oil. This happens because each acts according to its weight, finding its right level. When things are displaced, they are always on the move until they come to rest where they are meant to be. In my case, love is the weight by which I act. To whatever place I go, I am drawn to it by love. By your Gift, the Holy Ghost, we are set aflame and borne aloft, and the fire within us carries us upward. *Our hearts are set on an upward journey,* as we sing the *song of ascents*. It is your fire, your good fire, that sets us aflame and carries us upward. For our journey leads us upward to the peace of the heavenly Jerusalem; *it was a welcome sound when I heard them saying, We will go into the Lord's house.* There, if our will is good, you will find room for us, so that we shall wish for nothing else but to remain in your house for ever. (Translated by R. S. Pine-Coffin, Penguin Classics.)

*

In this introduction I have preferred to concentrate on what influenced the writing of *The New Life* and what can be known from it. Had I space, I would gladly write at even greater length on the influence it has exerted upon European literature and society, of the tradition which, carried on by Petrarch and Boccaccio, was fused with Greek learning in the Florentine academy. However, the name of Dante is its own recommendation, and the name of Beatrice is known to millions who do not know 'what it is they call her'.

I have translated the poems into a verse whose aim is to produce in English a music equivalent to the glorious sounds which Dante assembled in his work. It is impossible to reproduce his hendecasyllabic line in English simply because our language does not possess enough light feminine endings to its words. *The New Life* has already been translated into English common metre, in the famous version of Dante Gabriel Rossetti, and thus there seemed no point in employing that form. There is a third consideration for using an unusual verse form, and that is to re-create in part the sense of something new which the poems of *The New Life* inspired in Dante's contemporaries. On the other hand, I have tried to keep as much as possible to his rhyme schemes and the visual shape of his poems.

If anyone finds difficulty in reading these versions, let him read one of them aloud, concentrating while he does so as much on the direction of the sense as on the music of the words. In this way I hope he will understand the reasons for their construction.

INTRODUCTION

I owe many thanks to J. M. Cohen for his guidance and helpful suggestions. I was also fortunate enough to enjoy the help of Signor Leone Vivante, whose sympathy and understanding of English poetry turned his criticisms into the most profitable aids in revising the poems. My wife, to whom I have dedicated my own work in this version, and Mrs Marjorie Muir have both given me the greatest help. I must thank the Harvard University Press as publisher for the Dante Society for permission to quote the passage on page 17.

WILLIAM ANDERSON

THE NEW LIFE

I

EARLY on in the book of my memory[1] – almost before anything else can be read there – is a rubric which says: 'The New Life begins.' Under this rubric I find written the words which I intend to reassemble in this short book; or if not all of them, at least their meaning.

II

SINCE the time of my birth[2] the heaven of light had performed nine revolutions returning almost to the same point, when my eyes first lit upon the glorious lady of my mind[3] who was called Beatrice by many who did not know what it was they called her.

1. The whole of this work is contained within the metaphor of the Book of Memory. Dante increased his own objectivity by acting as a commentator or gloss-writer on the events recorded in this metaphorical book. This prologue should be kept in mind for when the reader comes to the passage (p. 89) where Dante gives his reasons for not describing the death of Beatrice.

2. 'Since the time of my birth': The heaven of light is the heaven of the sun, the fourth heaven in the scale of the nine moving heavens, according to the cosmology upon which *The New Life* is based.

3. 'The glorious lady of my mind': In the original Dante uses the word *gloriosa*, which would have signified to a reader of his time that Beatrice was already dead, before Dante had time to tell him. The passage following, 'who was called Beatrice by many who did not know what it was they called her', is very vexed. It can either mean that she was called 'Beatrice', the 'bestower of blessings', by people who did not know her true name; or else that those who called her Beatrice did not understand how truly suitable a name it was for her.

She had already been in this life so long that the starry heaven[1] had moved towards the orient one twelfth part of a degree, so that she was just eight when she first appeared to me, and I was almost nine. She was dressed in a noble colour of subdued and plain crimson, girdled and adorned as suited her early years. At that moment, I am speaking in all truth, the spirit of life[2] which lives in the most secret room of the heart began to vibrate so fiercely that its effect was dreadfully apparent in the least of my pulses; and, trembling, it said these words: 'Behold a God Who is stronger than I, Who in His coming will govern me.'

At that moment the spirit of perception which lives in the high room to which all the spirits of the senses carry their messages began to wonder greatly; and, speaking especially to the spirit of sight, it said these words: 'Your blessing has now appeared.'

At that moment the instinctive spirit which lives in the part where our food is digested began to weep; and in weeping it said: 'Alas! for from now on I shall suffer frequent checks.' From that time onwards Love held dominion over my soul, which was thus bound to him early in life. He began to exert over me such care and such mastery,

1. 'The starry heaven': The eighth heaven, that of the fixed stars, which is here connected with the life of Beatrice. The angelic order associated with this heaven is that of the Cherubim, the images of heavenly wisdom. Thus Dante stresses his own inferiority to her, since his life is connected to the lesser heaven of the sun. The moving of the starry heaven refers to the precession of the equinoxes, and it has been calculated from the directions Dante gives that Beatrice was eight years and four months old when he first saw her on 1 May 1274.

2. 'The spirit of life': This is the seat of the emotions, through which Dante was first struck by his love of Beatrice. Next comes the recognition by the intellect through the means of sense perception acknowledging her to be his blessing. Then, last of all, his instinctive centre becomes conscious of the bodily turmoil brought by this love.

through the power my imagination lent him, that I was forced to carry out all his wishes absolutely. He often ordered me to go and look for this young angel, and so in my boyhood I sought her many times. She struck me as being so noble and praiseworthy in her bearing that the words of the poet Homer[1] could certainly be applied to her: 'She seemed to be the daughter not of a mortal but of God.' Her image, remaining in me always, was so pure that, however exuberant Love grew, he was never allowed to force me against the faithful advice of reason whenever that advice was useful.

Since talking about things done and endured at so early an age generally has an air of fiction, I shall leave them. Passing by many things which are written in the book from which these are drawn, I shall look at those which are found in my memory under more important headings.

III

NINE years had passed[2] since this first meeting I have described with my glorious lady when, on the actual anniversary, it happened that this miraculous lady appeared to me, clothed in pure white, and walking between two older women. As she passed along the road she turned her eyes to where in fear and trembling I stood. Then out of her inexpressible courtesy, which now receives its reward in heaven, she greeted me so graciously that at that moment I seemed to experience absolute blessedness.

The hour when she greeted me was in fact nine o'clock; and as it was the first time she had spoken to me, I was so

1. Dante knew Homer only from a résumé in Latin.
2. 'Nine years had passed': This second meeting is dated 1 May 1283, when Dante was almost eighteen.

overcome by her sweetness that I left the crowds like a drunkard and went to be alone in my room. There I set myself to reflect on her courtesy.

IV

As I thought of her, a gentle sleep fell upon me in which I saw a remarkable vision. I thought a flame-coloured cloud appeared in my room, and in it I saw the figure of a lord,[1] terrifying to anyone who should look at him. The delight he seemed to take in himself was quite strange. He said many things to me, of which I understood little, amongst them being: 'I am your lord.' In his arms I saw a woman sleeping, naked apart from a blood-coloured cloth lightly wrapped around her. As I looked at her closely, I recognized the lady of the salutation, who had greeted me on the day before. In one of his hands he held something that was all on fire, and he said: 'Behold your heart.' When he had stayed there some time, he awoke the sleeping woman and forced her to eat the burning thing in his hand; and she ate it, with great misgivings. In a short time his joyfulness changed to the bitterest weeping; and so, lamenting, he clasped the lady in his arms and turned away with her up towards heaven. At this, my anguish was so great that my light sleep could not withstand it, and I awoke. Immediately I began to reflect and I discovered that the time when this vision appeared to me was the fourth hour of the night.

Thinking about this vision, I decided to make it known to

1. The first vision in which Love appears to Dante foreshadows the entire course of events to come. Love awakens from her sleep the woman who is both Beatrice and the New Life; he forces her to eat Dante's heart, thus symbolizing the gradual attachment of his life to her; and then carries her with him to heaven, a warning of her approaching death.

the many famous poets of that time; and as I had already learned the art of writing verses, I decided to compose a sonnet in which I would salute all the faithful servants of Love. So, describing the vision I had seen in my sleep and asking them to interpret it, I began this sonnet.

THE FIRST SONNET

To every captive soul and gentle heart abroad
  Who for this present verse has eyes,
  That they may send me their replies,
Greetings in the name of Love, their lord.

Already a third of the hours had passed
  Of the time when every star is bright,
  When Love appeared in sudden light,
Whose essence in memory leaves me aghast.

Happy seemed Love to me, keeping
  My heart in his hand; he bore in his arms
  My lady, wrapped in a cloth and sleeping.

Then he awoke her; and she humbly obeying
  Ate my heart of flame with fearful qualms.
  Then I saw him go on his way, weeping.

This sonnet divides into two parts. In the first part I give my greetings and ask for a reply, and in the second I say what it is that needs answering. The second part begins at 'Already a third . . .'

This sonnet received replies from many who took it in different senses, and amongst them was the man I now call my best friend,[1] who sent me a sonnet which starts: 'I believe you beheld all goodness . . .'

Our friendship dates almost from the moment I learned it was he who had sent me this sonnet.

V

FROM the time of this vision onwards my body began to suffer in its workings, so much was my mind taken up with thinking about my gentle lady. Thus in a short time I became quite thin and weak, and many of my friends were troubled at the sight of me. Others, prompted by malice, went so far as to ask me whether I had anything to hide from other people. Perceiving the spirit of malicious curiosity which made them ask, by the will of Love, who guided me according to the advice of reason, I replied that it was Love who had brought me to this state. I said Love, because I bore so many of his signs in my features that it could not be concealed. When they asked me 'Through whom has Love so destroyed you?', I would look at them, smile, and say nothing.

It chanced one day that this gentlest of women was sitting in church at a time when people were listening to words in praise of the Blessed Virgin. I was there too, in a position from which I could watch my beatitude. Another lady, very pleasing to look at, happened to be sitting in the direct line between us, and she stared at me often, wondering at my

1. The 'best friend' was Guido Cavalcanti, Dante's elder contemporary, for whom *The New Life* was written. It was he who insisted that it should be written in Italian, not Latin. Cavalcanti (c. 1260–1300) was the most original and accomplished poet of the time apart from Dante, and his deep interest in philosophy, the knowledge he gained from travelling widely, and his belief that only the gentle heart experiences love had a great influence on Dante. About thirty of his poems survive.

gaze, which seemed to be directed at her. Many people followed the direction of her looks. This was noticed so much
that as I was leaving the church I heard someone behind me
say: 'See how that woman is driving him to desperation.'
As he named her I realized that he meant the lady who was
in the middle of the direct line which started at the gentle
Beatrice and ended in my eyes. I drew great comfort from
this because I was assured that my secret had not been
betrayed that day by my looks.

Immediately I decided to make this lady a disguise of the
real truth, and I managed this so well that in a short time
many more than those who had spoken to me thought
themselves in possession of my secret. I hid my real thoughts
behind this lady for several months and years, and to add
credence to this belief I wrote her several trifles in verse,
which I do not intend to write out here except where they
touch on my gentle Beatrice. And so I shall leave them all
except those in which I wrote anything which seemed to
praise her.

VI

DURING the period that this lady acted as a disguise to so
much love on my part, I wanted to celebrate the name of
Beatrice and to accompany it with the names of many ladies,
especially the name of this lady. So I took the names of the
sixty most beautiful women in the city[1] where God had
placed my lady and I composed a letter in the form of a
serventese[2], which I shall not bother to copy out. I would
not have mentioned it except to say that while I was writing

1. The poem which Dante wrote in praise of the sixty ladies of
Florence has not survived.

2. A *serventese* was a simplified Italian version of a Provençal
verse-form called a *sirvente*.

it a most wonderful thing happened: my làdy's name would not allow itself to take any other position among all those ladies' names except that of ninth.

VII

THE lady whom I had used for so long to conceal my true feeling was forced to leave this city and go to a distant part of the country. As a consequence, being rather dismayed at the loss of this fine disguise, I was far more disturbed by it than I would have thought possible. As I thought people would guess the deceit all the sooner if l did not make known my sorrow at her departure, l decided to compose a lamentation in the form of a sonnet.[1] This I shall write down, since my lady was the immediate cause of certain words in the sonnet. The sonnet is as follows.

THE SECOND SONNET

O you who travel down Love's way
  Stop awhile and say
  If a grief can be found like mine;
  I ask you only to hear my song
  And then think long
If l am the inn and key to every pain.

Love, not for my desert at all
  But from his noble soul,
  Made life so sweet in every part
  That I often heard it said by one:
  'What has he done
  To deserve so happy a heart?'

1. This is a double sonnet, like the fourth sonnet. The second part probably refers to Beatrice, while the lament for the loss of the other lady is contained in the last quatrains.

Now my confidence is all lost
  Which drew on Love's treasury
  Leaving me in such poverty
I tremble to tell the cost.

So I, wishing to do like those
  Who conceal their lack from shame,
  To the world all joy proclaim
But my heart still wastes in woes.

This sonnet has two principal parts: in the first I call upon the faithful followers of Love in the words of the Prophet Jeremiah: 'Is it nothing to you, all you that pass by? Behold and see whether there be any sorrow like unto my sorrow.' And I beg them to listen to me. In the second part I tell where Love had placed me, with a meaning other than that shown by the last section of the sonnet, and I say what I have lost. The second part starts: 'Love, not for my desert at all . . .'

VIII

AFTER that lady's departure, the Lord of Angels was pleased to call to his glory a young lady who was lovely to look upon and who had graced this city considerably. I saw her lifeless body lying in the midst of a crowd of women, who were weeping for her with great sorrow. When I recalled that I had seen her in the company of Beatrice, I could not restrain my tears. In weeping, I decided to write some words about her death, as a token of having sometimes seen her with my lady. I touched on this in the last words I wrote, as will be obvious to any man with insight. So I wrote these two sonnets, the first of which begins 'Weep, all you lovers . . .', and the second 'Cruel Death . . .'.

THE THIRD SONNET

Weep, all you lovers, for Love himself weeps,
  When you hear his cause of lamenting:
  Love hears the women pitifully crying
As grief their eyes in bitterness steeps;

Because foul Death has worked upon her,
  Has worked on her heart his cruel ways,
  Wasting all that the world ought to praise
In a lovely lady, apart from honour.

Hear the triumph performed her by Love
  For I saw him in his true guise bemoan,
  Bending over her beautiful dead face;

And he gazed straight up to heaven above
  Where her noble soul already was known
  Which once was a lady of such sweet grace.

This first sonnet can be divided into three parts. In the first I call on and beg the faithful followers of Love to weep, and I say 'When you hear his cause of lamenting' so that they may be forced all the more to listen to me; in the second part I give the reason, and in the third I speak of the honour paid this lady by Love. The second part begins 'Love hears . . .', and the third 'Hear the triumph . . .'.

THE FOURTH SONNET

Cruel Death, compassion's foe,
  Ancient mother of all woe,
    Conquering judge without compare;
    Since you have brought a poor heart care
    And thought as I fare,
My tongue grows tired of cursing you.

To take from you all hint of good
  I want it ever understood
  That you are guilty of every sin
  – Not that this is ever hidden –
  But to arouse the wrath of men
Who find in Love their food.

You have cast gentleness from the earth
  And also virtue, woman's worth, and truth;
  In the joy of youth
You have ruined its loving mirth.

What lady this was, I shall not say;
  Let her virtues tell, here given;
  He who does not deserve to gain heaven
May never hope for her company.

This sonnet divides into four parts. In the first I call Death by some of his fitting names; in the second part I address him, giving my reasons for cursing him; in the third I abuse him; in the fourth I speak to someone unnamed although defined in the context of my meaning. The second part begins 'Since you have brought a poor heart care . . .', the third 'To take from you . . .', and the fourth 'He who does not deserve to gain heaven . . .'.

IX

SOME days after the death of this lady something occurred which made me leave the city. I had to go towards the district where the lady who had acted as my disguise was living, although my journey did not take me so far. Even though I was accompanied by many people, the journey so displeased me that my sighs could scarcely give vent to the agony my heart felt because I was travelling away from the seat of my blessedness. And so the Lord who ruled me through the power of my lovely Beatrice appeared to me in my imagination as a pilgrim thinly clothed in rags. He seemed to me in great distress and kept his gaze fixed on the ground except when, from time to time, he would turn towards a beautiful river, flowing with the clearest water,[1] which ran parallel to the road on which I was.

It seemed to me that Love called me and said these words: 'I come from the lady who has been your disguise for so long, and I know that she will not return for a long time. Therefore I have brought back the heart I made you for her, and I am carrying it to the lady who will be your disguise in future, as was once the other. (And he gave me her name, so that I could make no mistake.) But if you repeat anything of what I have said to you, put it in such a way that the pretence of love which you have shown her, and which you will now have to show to another, cannot be penetrated.' With these words everything in my imagination suddenly vanished because of the great part of himself that Love seemed to give me. As though transformed in my own eyes, I rode the rest of that day in thought and sighing often.

The next day I began this sonnet about it.

1. The image of clear flowing water is used twice in *The New Life*, on both occasions accompanying the introduction of a new factor. Here the new thing is the second 'disguise' lady; in the other instance it is connected with the inspiration of the first canzone. This image was a favourite one with Dante, and occurs frequently in *The Divine Comedy*.

Here too we find the introduction of the pilgrim theme which runs throughout the work. This will be discussed later.

THE FIFTH SONNET

While riding the other day along a road,
  I thought of the journey which caused me dismay
  When I saw Love in the middle of the way
In a pilgrim's habit thinly clothed.

His aspect, I thought, was sad and grim
  As though he had lost all his fame,
  And sighing and brooding he came,
Head down so men could not see him.

He called my name when he saw me,
  Saying: 'I come from a far country
  Where to please me lived your heart;

Which I return, to serve new pleasure now.'
  Then I took from him so great a part,
  He vanished and I could not see how.

This sonnet has three parts: in the first I say how I came upon Love and how he appeared to me; in the second I tell what he said to me, although not everything, for fear of revealing my secret; in the third I say how he vanished before me. The second part begins 'He called my name . . .', and the third 'Then I took . . .'.

X

AFTER my return I set out to find this lady whom my lord had named on the road of sighs. To cut the story as short as possible, very soon I had made such a disguise of her that far too many people made it a matter of rude gossip, and this often weighed heavily upon me. For this reason – I mean this malicious rumour, which viciously defamed me – the gentlest of all women, who was the destroyer of all vices and the queen of virtue, as she passed along a certain way, denied me that sweet greeting in which the whole of my blessedness lay. Digressing a little from my present purpose, I would like to make clear the wonderful power her greeting had over me.

XI

WHEN in any way she appeared, just through the hope of receiving her marvellous greeting, I had no enemies left but was instead possessed by such a flame of charity that I was made to forgive all those who had injured me; and if at that moment someone had asked me a question about any matter in the world, my answer, with my face clothed in humility, would have been quite simply: 'Love.' Then as she drew near to give her greeting, one spirit of Love, destroying all the other spirits of perception, would cast out the weak spirits of sight and say to them 'Go to honour your lady,' while he himself remained in their place. If any one had wished to study Love, he could have done so by watching the quivering of my eyes. When this gentlest of women gave her greeting, Love by no means overshadowed the unendurable blessedness, but indeed grew to such power by a superabundance of rapture that my body, being completely under his domination, often felt like a dead weight. From this it is obvious that my blessedness dwelt in her greeting, which was frequently more than I could endure.

XII

NOW, returning to what I was saying, after my blessedness was denied me, I was overcome by such sorrow that I left my fellow men and went to a secluded place, where I could bathe the earth with my bitter tears. Then when my weeping was almost exhausted, I took myself to my room, where I could lament without being overheard. There, while calling for mercy from the lady of courtesy, and crying 'Love, help your servant!', I fell asleep like a little child crying after it has been beaten.

At about half-way through my sleep, I thought I saw a young man who was clothed in pure white and who seemed sunk in deep reflection. He gazed at where I lay and after doing so for some time he seemed to sigh and call my name, uttering these words: 'My son, it is time we put an end to our dissimulations.'[1] Then it suddenly struck me that I recognized him, because he called me just as he had done many times before in my dreams.

As I returned his gaze I could see that he was weeping pitifully and seemed to expect some reply from me. Gathering my senses together I started to address him thus: 'Lord of excellence, why do you weep so?' And he answered with these words: 'I am like the centre of a circle,[2] from which all parts of the circumference are equally distant; but it is not so with you.' When I pondered on his words, I thought

1. 'My son, it is time we put an end to our dissimulation': In this sentence, which is in Latin in the original, comes the word *simulacra,* which means 'images of a god' as well as dissimulations. Thus it can be taken to mean that the time has come for Dante to make another step towards divine love and to do away with a false conception.

2. 'I am like the centre of a circle': These words inevitably recall the ancient description of God as an infinite sphere whose centre is everywhere and whose circumference nowhere. Love's words may be taken as meaning that he has full knowledge of what is to come – i.e. the death of Beatrice – since he sees life from outside mortal time, which binds Dante.

he had spoken very obscurely, so that I forced myself to ask him: 'Lord, why have you spoken so obscurely to me?' But he answered in my own language: 'Ask no more than is useful to you.'

Then I began to discuss with him the greeting which had been denied to me, and to ask the reason. His reply was like this: 'Our Beatrice heard from certain people who were discussing you that the lady whom I named to you, on the road of sighs, had received some injury from you. Therefore this gentlest of women, who is the very opposite of all injury, did not deign to greet you, fearing that it might be sinful. Since, however, she is partly aware of your secret, through long association, I want you to say certain things in verse in which you will explain the power I wield over you through her, and how you have belonged to her ever since your boyhood. In doing this, call as a witness the one who knows all this, and say how you beg him to repeat it to her. I, who am that very one, will willingly speak of it to her; thus she will understand your wish and also the words of the gossipers. Write your poem so that it can act as an intermediary, and do not address her directly, because that would not be fitting. Also do not send it where she may hear it without me, but accompany it with gentle music, in which I shall be present whenever necessary.'

With these words he vanished, and my sleep was broken. Recollecting myself, I realized that this vision had appeared to me at the ninth hour of the day. Before I left my room I intended to write a ballad, in which I would include everything my lord had ordered; and so I wrote this ballad.[1]

1. The opening quatrain of this ballad is the refrain to each of the succeeding stanzas.

THE FIRST BALLAD

Ballad, I want you to find out Love again
   And go to my lady's presence,
So my lord pleads my defence
   Which you can sing to his strain.

Ballad, you act with such courtesy
   That unattended
You could make bold in any place;
   But if you want true safety,
Be by Love befriended.
It would be foolish without his grace;
   For she who should hear your stated case,
If she condemns me as I fear
   And you are not in Love's care,
Would treat you with scorn and disdain.

When you meet him and ask her mercy,
   While sweet sounds play,
Utter this oration:
   'My lady, I am on embassy
From one who desires me to say
   – If you allow him an explanation –
That I should fulfil his duty.
   It is Love, because your beauty,
Who makes his expression so change.
   Can you think how his eyes might range
While his heart has not veered again?'

Tell her: 'My lady, his heart has ever
   Been grounded in such firm faith
That every thought spurs him on to your service.
   He was yours from a child, without one waver.'

If she grants this no belief
  Tell her love will give true advice.
Then make this last request for solace:
  If she considers she may not forgive,
Let me be told I may not live
  And behold! her slave submits to Death's bane.

Then say to Love, the key to pity,
  Before you withdraw from her
– For he will tell what excuses I have –
  'By the grace of my music's purity
Remain here with her
  And say what you think best for your slave.
Then if she pardons him when you crave
  Ensure peace is made in a gracious greeting.'
My gentle ballad, when you are fleeting,
  Act so you gather both honour and gain.

This ballad divides into three parts; in the first I tell the ballad where it must go, comforting it so that it travels more safely, and I say whose company it must adopt if it wants to avoid danger; in the second part I give the message it should convey, while in the third I grant it permission to wander where it wishes, commending its journey to the arms of fortune. The second part begins 'When you meet him', and the third 'My gentle ballad . . .'.

An objection might be made that it is not clear who it is I address in the second person, since the ballad itself is nothing but the words I speak. Since I intend to solve this difficulty in an even more obscure passage in this short work, let those who fail to understand or who wish to object, be enlightened then.[1]

1. Dante's explanation of his personification of inanimate objects or attributes is to be found on pages 82–4.

XIII

It was after this vision, and when I had already composed the poem ordered by Love, that many conflicting thoughts began to fight for possession of me. All these thoughts left me almost defenceless, but among them there were four especially which disturbed the calm of my life. One of these went as follows: 'The domination of Love is good, because it draws the minds of his faithful followers away from baser things.' Another was this: 'The domination of Love is not good, since the more his followers submit to him the greater are the pains and miseries they have to endure.' The next one was like this: 'The name of Love is so charming to hear, and it seems to me impossible that its workings could be anything but sweet, since names follow after the things they name, as it is written: *Nomina sunt consequentia rerum.*' The fourth was this: 'The lady through whom Love so binds you is not like other women, who can touch only the surface of the heart.' Each of these thoughts struggled within me to such an extent that I was like a man who cannot choose which road to take, who wants very much to travel but does not know the direction. If I tried to find a way suitable for all of them, on which they could agree, this was a way quite abhorrent to me, for it meant I had to call on Pity and to surrender myself to her arms. While I remained in this state, the desire came upon me to write a poem and so I composed this sonnet.

THE SIXTH SONNET

Love is the theme of my thought's discussion
But they disagree between them all four,
For one thinks Love means madness in store
While another desires my total submission.

Another brings joy with hope for its part;
  Another makes me weep often and bitterly;
  They agree only in demanding pity
Trembling at the fear in my heart.

So the doubtful decisions rend me,
  Wanting to speak, incapable utterly;
  Thus I live in Love's great bewilderment
  Where if I want all thoughts in agreement
  I am forced to call on my worst enemy,
My lady Pity, that she may defend me.

This sonnet can be divided into four parts. In the first I state that all my thoughts are concerned with Love; in the second I explain their differences; in the third I say what they are agreed upon; the fourth deals with my dilemma in wishing to speak of Love and yet not knowing what argument to take; if I want to reconcile them all, I am driven to demand help from my lady Pity. I call her 'my lady' in a scornful way of address. The second part begins 'But they disagree . . .', the third 'They agree only . . .', and the fourth 'So the doubtful decisions . . .'.

XIV

AFTER this battle of conflicting thoughts, this gentlest of women happened to be present at a gathering of many ladies of noble birth. A friend of mine took me there, thinking he would give me great pleasure with the sight of so many women displaying their beauty. I, equally wishing to give pleasure to my friend, proposed that we should remain and wait on the ladies. Since I hardly knew where I should be taken, and trusted my companion, who had supported one of his friends to his last hour, I said to him: 'Why are we going to these ladies?' And he answered: 'To see that they are properly attended.'

In fact the gathering was to accompany a young woman who had been married that morning. According to the custom of this city, these ladies were to accompany her when she sat down for the first time at table in the house of her bridegroom. When I had made this proposal, I felt a strange trembling begin in the left side of my breast and suddenly spread throughout all my body. To disguise this I had to lean against a fresco which ran round the walls of that house. Fearing others would notice my trembling, I raised my eyes and, looking at the ladies, saw Beatrice among them. Then were my faculties so destroyed by the force Love drew from my proximity to this gentlest of women, that all were deprived of life, except my perceptions of sight, and even they were driven out of my eyes, because Love wished to stand in their privileged place so that he could see her better. Although I felt entirely altered, I still grieved for those perceptions, which lamented loudly and said: 'If he had not expelled us from our place, we could have seen the wonder of this lady, as our equals do.'

Many of these ladies, struck with my transformation, began to marvel at it. Talking to this gentlest of women, they mocked at me; and so my friend, who had no understanding of what had happened, took me by the hand and drew me out of the sight of the women, asking what was the matter. Having recovered myself a little by that time, when my dead perceptions were raised again and those which had been dispersed had returned to their functions, I said to my friend: 'I have set my feet on that part of life from which there is no return.'

Leaving him I returned to my sad room, where, weeping and overcome with shame, I said to myself: 'If she realized my true condition, I do not believe she would mock me, but instead would look on me with compassion.' While making this complaint, I decided to write something which would explain the cause of my transformation to her; and I wanted to say that I knew very well its cause could not be known to her for, if it were, others would be moved to pity by it. I said this in the wish that it might come to her hearing. Then I wrote this sonnet.

THE SEVENTH SONNET

With other women you mock at my sight
  And do not think, lady, how it can be,
  When I gaze at your riches of beauty
That my expression could change at its might.

If you realized this, compassion could
  No longer resist in her old manner;
  For Love when he finds us both together
Takes on so bold and assuming a mood

That he strikes my weak spirits of sense,
  Killing some, driving others away,
  So that he only is left to admire you:

Thus I am changed to another's hue
  But not so much that I no longer may
  Hear the fugitives' moans and laments.

I have not divided this sonnet into parts, because a division is made only to make the meaning clearer, and since its argument is obvious enough I have not bothered to do so.

It is true that there are obscure words among those which describe the origin of the sonnet; namely when I state that Love kills all my perceptions except those of sight, which remain alive but are driven from their habitation. This obscurity is impossible to clarify to any one who has not reached an equal rank as a servant of Love; those of you who have done so possess the key to the difficulty. Therefore it would be useless for me to attempt an explanation since my speaking would be fruitless and indeed superfluous.

XV

AFTER this latest transformation, I was possessed by an idea of great power, which rarely left me. It returned constantly to my thoughts and took this form: 'Since you meet with such contempt when you go near this lady, why do you attempt to see her? Now look, if she asked you something, what would you reply, granted that you preserved your power over your faculty of speech?' This was replied to by another humble thought, which said: 'If I did not lose my faculties, and were free to answer her, I would say that the moment I form a picture in my mind of her marvellous beauty, I am seized by a desire to see her. This desire is so strong that it kills and destroys everything in my memory which could rise up to oppose it. Therefore my past sufferings cannot stop my trying to see her.' Moved by these ideas, I intended to write something in which, after making my excuse, I should tell her what overcame me when I was near her. So I composed this sonnet.

THE EIGHTH SONNET

All memories of what has happened vanish
  When I approach your beauty and rejoice,
  Till I am near and I hear Love's voice
Saying: 'Flee if you fear to perish!'

My heart's colours to my countenance fly;
 Fainting, it demands some relief.
 Drunk with its tremor, in my belief,
The very stones shriek: 'Die! Die!'

He is a sinner who does not attempt
 To calm my soul's terror and dread,
 Even by showing his heart is rent

Because of the pity which your scorn slays
 And which is born in the deathly glaze
 Of eyes which desire to be dead.

This sonnet divides into two parts. In the first I say why
I am not deterred from going near this lady, and in the second
I say what happens to me when I approach her; the second
part begins at 'Till I am near . . .'. This second part
can be subdivided into five, according to five different inter-
pretations; in the first of these I say that Love, with the
advice of reason warns me when I am near her; in the second
I reveal the state of my heart by the colour of my face; in
the third I tell how all confidence leaves me; in the fourth I
call the man a sinner who does not comfort me out of pity;
and in the last I say why one ought to have pity, and this is
because of the anguished look which comes over my eyes.
The effect of this look is destroyed by the mocking of this
lady, who makes anyone who might be touched by it do as
she does. The second part begins 'My heart's colours . . .',
the third 'Drunk with its tremor . . .', the fourth 'He is a
sinner . . .', and the fifth 'Because of the pity . . .'.

XVI

AFTER I had composed this sonnet, the desire came upon
me to write something else, in which I could describe four

things about my condition which I had not explained before. The first is that I was caused much grief whenever my memory recalled to my imagination Love's treatment of me. The next thought is that Love frequently attacked me so fiercely that nothing in me remained alive except one thought, which spoke of my lady. The next was that when Love's assault had thus laid me waste, I set out, almost completely drained of colour, to see this lady. I believed that the sight of her would defend me from the attack, forgetting what had happened to me from approaching her gentleness. The last thought is how this sight of her not only did not defend me but defeated what little life remained to me. Therefore I wrote this sonnet.

THE NINTH SONNET

There often returns to my inward eye
    That dark condition which Love bestows,
    And pity so touches me I have to cry:
'Alas! have others received such blows?'

For Love attacks with such sudden strife
    The soul almost leaves my frame:
    One spirit only escapes with life
And that because it utters your name.

Then do I force myself, wanting aid anew
    And like a dead man empty of strength
    Come to you to be cured of my pains;

But if I raise my eyes towards you
    A quaking within my heart at length
    Drives the soul from my beating veins.

This sonnet divides into the four subjects it deals with; since I have already discussed them, I will only point out where each part begins: the second part 'For Love . . .', the third 'Then do I force . . .', and the fourth 'But if I raise my eyes . . .'.

XVII

WHEN I had related nearly my whole condition to this lady in these three sonnets, and though I thought I would hold my peace, because I had spoken quite enough about myself, even if it meant not addressing her, I was forced to turn to a subject fresher and more noble than any I had touched before. Since the origin of this fresh material is delightful to hear, I will relate it as briefly as possible.

XVIII

MY heart's secret had been revealed to many people by my countenance, and so certain ladies who had gathered together for the pleasure of one another's company understood the state of my heart, because they had been present at several of its reverses. As I, led on by chance, was passing them, one of these gentle ladies, of especially charming speech, called me. When I joined them and saw that my lady was not among them, I took courage, greeted them, and asked what I could do for them. There were several ladies there, some of whom were laughing among themselves. Others stood waiting for me to speak, while there were some who talked together. One of these, turning her eyes towards me and calling my name, said these words: 'What is the aim of your love, since you cannot endure your lady's presence? Tell us, for such a reason must be very strange indeed.' The moment she said these words, all the others turned to await my reply. Then I said to them: 'The aim of my love was once the greeting I received from my lady, of whom you perhaps are thinking. My blessedness dwelt in that, and it was the end of all my desires. But since she has been pleased to deny it me, my lord, Love, out of his mercy, has placed all my experience of blessedness where it cannot fail me.'

Then these ladies began to talk among themselves; and, as we sometimes see rain falling mingled with lovely snow, so I seemed to hear their words interleaved with sighs. When they had spoken together a little, the lady who had first addressed me asked: 'We beg you to say in what your blessedness dwells.' My answer was this: 'In those words which praise my lady.' And she replied: 'If you had spoken truly, your poems describing your condition to us would have been constructed differently.'

Reflecting on these words, I left them as though ashamed of myself. As I walked, I said to myself: 'Since there is such blessedness in those words which praise my lady, why have I spoken of anything else?' Therefore I resolved to take for my subject-matter only the praise of this gentlest of women. Pondering this, it struck me that I had undertaken a task far beyond my ability and did not dare begin; thus I remained several days, wanting to write and yet afraid of starting.

XIX

THEN it happened that I was walking along a road beside which flowed a river of clear water; and it was there that such a desire to speak seized me that I began to consider what style I should adopt. I thought it would not be fitting to address her directly but to speak of her to ladies in the second person; even then not to all ladies but only to those who are noble and not mere women. Then my tongue spoke as though moved by itself and said: 'Ladies whose understanding is of Love . . .'. I laid these words before my mind with the greatest joy, intending to use them as my beginning. Then I returned to the city and after pondering for some days I began a canzone with that beginning, constructed in the following way.[1]

THE FIRST CANZONE

Ladies whose understanding is of Love
* I want to tell you of my lady,*
*   Not because I can praise her fully,*
But by discussion to clear my mind.

I say that in reflecting on her worth
* Love has extended his charmed reach*
*   That, had I still courage, just by my speech*
To Love all men would be inclined.

So I must avoid that great elation
* Lest fear should sully me with its taint;*
*   But treating her with sure restraint*
I shall relate her gentle station,
* Loving ladies and girls, to you;*
*   It is only for the ears of the few.*

An angel in the divine intellect calls,
* Saying: 'Lord, there is in the world*
*   A wonder in action now unfurled*
From a soul whose light here soars.'

1. This canzone, which marks the beginning of the second phase of events narrated in *The New Life*, aroused great contemporary interest.

Heaven which has no lack in its halls
  Except her, begs God for her possession,
  And every saint cries for satisfaction;
Only Compassion defends our cause.

God now speaks with my lady in mind:
  'My chosen people, endure My will.
  As it pleases Me, she remains still
Where a man lives,[1] to her loss resigned,
  Who shall say in Hell; "O sons of pest,
  I have looked on the hope of the blest." '

My lady is desired in the height of heaven;
  Let all her virtues be known through me.
  I say: whoever wishes to be a noble lady
Should walk with her; for as she goes
Love ices the hearts of wicked men,
  So all their thoughts are frozen and wither.
  Whoever is able to stand and regard her
Becomes transfigured or else he dies.

When she chances to find a man worthy
  Of seeing her, her power is displayed,
  For she gives a greeting and he is made
So humble, all sins leave his memory.
  For God has granted such grace to her will
  He who speaks to her meets no ill.

Love says of her, 'How can a mortal thing
  Have beauty and purity in such wealth?'
  He looks at her, swearing to himself:
'God meant her as a new creation.

1. 'Where a man lives . . . who shall say in Hell': Not unnaturally, this passage has been seen as the germ of the *Inferno*, though whether Dante had at this early stage a conception of his later work cannot now be known.

Her form has just that pearl colouring
    Which suits a woman, without excess.
    She is nature's summit of goodness
And beauty is judged by her perfection.'

As she directs them, her eyes dart
    Flaming spirits of Love around,
    Which strike the sight of those there found
And drive so deep they reach the heart.
    You see Love's image in her smile,
    Where none can gaze for any while.

My song, I know you will have speech
    With many ladies when I have sped you.
    I must advise you, since I bred you
To be Love's daughter, young and guileless
That where you go you may beseech:
    'Tell me my way; for I am sent
    To her whose praise I here present.'
And if you want to act with purpose

Do not remain where people are brutes;
    Be understood only, if you can,
    By a gentle lady or courteous man,
Who will carry you the quickest routes.
    Love will be with her at your meeting;
    Commend me to him in your greeting.

So that this canzone can be better understood, I will divide it with greater care than before. It has three main divisions. The first part acts as prologue to what follows; the second part begins 'An angel . . .', and the third 'My song, I know . . .'. The first part subdivides into four; in the first I say to whom I wish to speak about my lady and why I do so; in the second subdivision I explain how I appear to myself when I reflect on her quality, and how I would speak of her if I had not lost my daring. In the third part I say how I manage to speak of her without being hindered by cowardice; and in the fourth I repeat who it is that I address, giving my reason for doing so. The second part begins 'I say . . .', the third 'So I must avoid . . .', and the fourth 'Loving ladies and girls . . .'.

Then, when I say 'An angel . . .', I start to speak of my lady, and this is subdivided into two. In the first part I say what is understood of her in Heaven, while the second tells what is thought of her on earth. This last part divides again into two, for in the first of these I describe the nobility of her soul and the virtues which proceed from it. At the second part, beginning 'Love says of her . . .', I describe the nobility of her body and its beauties.

This second part again divides into two, for in the first I speak of the general beauties of her body, while in the second, starting at 'As she directs . . .', I deal with the individual beauties.

The last part can in its turn be divided into two, because in one I speak of her eyes, which are the origin of Love, and in the next I describe her mouth which is the end of Love. To forestall any lewd thoughts, the reader should remember what has been written before, that it was the greeting issuing from my lady's mouth which was the end of all my desires, while I was still able to receive it.

Then, when I say 'My song, I know . . .', this is a stanza acting as a handmaiden to the others. Here I say what I want the canzone to do, and since this last part is simple to understand I will not bother to divide it.

I must indeed admit that even more precise divisions would be needed for this canzone to be understood further. However, if a man is not intelligent enough to comprehend it from those divisions I have already made, I do not mind if he lets it alone; for in fact I am afraid of having communicated too much of its meaning by what I have said already, if it should come to the ears of many people.

XX

AFTER this canzone had been made public, a certain friend of mine who had heard it begged me to describe Love to him; he had perhaps a greater opinion of me through this poem than I deserved. It struck me that after such a poem it would be pleasant to speak of Love. So, aware also of my duty to a friend, I decided to write something which dealt of Love, and thus I wrote this sonnet.

THE TENTH SONNET

Love is the same as a gentle heart
  – Such is the theme of the wise man[1] *–*
  They dare dwell no farther apart
Than the rational soul from reason.

Nature makes, when her mood is loving,
  Love the lord and the heart his house,
  In which he shelters slumbering
For as long or short as the season allows.

When beauty appears in a wise lady
  It delights the eyes, so the heart thereof
  Is sown with desire for such pleasure,

1. The 'wise man' referred to in the sonnet is Guido Guinizelli (c. 1240–76) the Bolognese poet. (See Introduction, p. 14.)

And there it sometimes abides so truly
That it awakens the spirit of Love;
Good men affect ladies in equal measure.

This sonnet divides into two parts. In the first I speak of
Love's potential existence and in the second I describe his
transformation from potentiality into actuality. The second
part starts 'When beauty appears . . .'. The first part subdivides into two, and in the first of these I say in what
subject this potentiality resides. In the second I tell how this
subject and potentiality are brought into being and how the
one is related to the other as form is to matter. The second
begins: 'Nature makes . . .'. Then, when I say 'When beauty
appears . . .', I describe the transformation of this potentiality
into actuality, first in a man and then, at 'Good men . . .',
in a lady.

XXI

When I had dealt with Love in this sonnet, the wish came
upon me to write more in praise of the gentlest of women. In
this I wanted to show how she not only awakens Love when
it sleeps but how she miraculously brings it forth even where
it does not exist in potentiality. So I wrote this sonnet.

THE ELEVENTH SONNET

My lady carries Love within her eyes,
And all they rest on come to calm;
Her walking binds men with a charm;
Whom she greets feels his heart's surprise.

He blanches in his downcast face
And sighs at his sins which gride;
Before her flee all anger and pride.
Help me, ladies, to honour her grace.

Every sweet and humble thought
  Is born in the heart at the sound of her voice.
Who first beholds her, his glory is sealed.

When lightly she smiles, what is revealed
  Cannot be told nor remembered by choice,
  So rare a miracle in her is wrought.

This sonnet has three parts. In the first I say how my lady brings the potentiality into actual being through the power of her eyes, while in the third I record the similar action of her mouth. Between these two parts is inserted a brief interlude which is a call for help for the preceding and following sections. This interlude starts 'Help me, ladies . . .', and the third part 'Every sweet and humble thought . . .'.

The first section divides into three. The beginning describes how the power of her virtue makes gentle all she sees, and this means that she brings Love into being where it did not exist in potentiality. In the second I say how she makes Love appear in the hearts of all those who see her. In the third I describe how strongly she affects their hearts. The second part begins 'Her walking binds . . .', and the third, 'Whom she greets . . .'.

When later I say 'Help me, ladies . . .', I make it clear to whom I am speaking in calling on them to do her honour. Then, when I say 'Every sweet and humble thought . . .', I relate what was said in the first part to the actions of her mouth; one of these is her charming speech and the other her miraculous smile. The effect of the latter, however, I cannot describe since it is impossible for the memory to retain it.

XXII

NOT many days later, as it pleased God, who Himself underwent the pains of death, the father of Beatrice[1] left this life, assuredly for eternal glory. Such a loss is always sorrowful to the remaining friends of the dead man, especially since there is no bond of love so intimate as that between a good father and a good child and a good child and a good father. As my lady was of the highest goodness, and her father, according to true report, nearly approached her in quality, it is understandable that she was overcome by the bitterest grief.

Therefore as it is customary in this city for women to meet with women and men with men at such a sad time, there were many ladies with Beatrice while she was piteously weeping. Seeing some ladies come away from her I heard them describe Beatrice's lamentations. Among what they said I caught these words: 'Certainly her sorrow is such that anyone seeing it is ready to die of compassion.' Then these ladies passed on, and I remained so stunned by misery that my face was bathed in tears and I was forced to hide my eyes with my hands. If I had not been expecting to hear more of her, since nearly all her visitors would pass by the place where I was standing, I should have fled the moment my tears began.

So while I remained there, more ladies passed by me, saying these words as they walked: 'Which of us can ever be happy again, now we have heard her speaking so heart-

1. The father of Beatrice was Folco Portinari, who died on 21 December 1289. He was noted in his lifetime for his good works. According to his will, Beatrice was by this time married to Simone de' Bardi.

breakingly?' Then came other ladies who said: 'That man there weeps as much as if he had seen her as we have done.' Then others said of me: 'He is so changed, he does not seem to be himself.' Thus while these ladies passed by I heard them speak of her and of me in this manner.

Reflecting on this, I determined to write something – for I had sufficient worth saying – in which I would include everything I had learned from these ladies. As I would willingly have asked them questions had the time been suitable, I wrote it in the form of my questioning and their answering.

So I made two sonnets; in the first I ask, in the way I had wanted to ask, and in the second I give their answer, taking what I had overheard as if it had been addressed to me. The first sonnet begins 'You who are wearing . . .', and the second 'Are you indeed . . .'.

THE TWELFTH SONNET

You who are wearing a humble mien
  Revealing your grief in eyes downcast,
  Whence do you come? What is it has passed?
That in your faces such pity is seen.

Have you beheld our gentle lady
  Bathe her face in the tears of love?
  Tell me, ladies, for my heart tells thereof,
As it sees you return gravely and sadly.

And if you come from such compassion,
  Remain here a while till you go,
  Concealing nothing of her condition.
For I see your eyes weep at her woe,

And I see in you such transformation
My heart shudders to witness you so.

This sonnet divides into two parts. In the first I call and
ask these ladies if they may have come from Beatrice, telling
them I suspect this because they seem ennobled by their
visit. And in the second part, which begins 'And if you
come . . .', I beg them to tell me how she is.

THE THIRTEENTH SONNET

Are you indeed the man who so often
Spoke of your lady to us alone?
Your voice resembles his in its tone,
But from other men your features seem taken.

Why do you weep with such heartfelt pain
That pity is aroused in all others?
Have you seen her weep, that nothing smothers
The grieving thoughts of your brain?

Leave to us weeping and procession
– He sins who attempts to bring solace –
For we have heard her at intercession.

She reveals her pity so clear in her face
That if any dared watch her, the mere impression
Would make them fall dead at that place.

This sonnet has four parts, just as the ladies for whom I
answer had four different phrases. Since they have already
been made clear enough, I will not bother to give their
meaning, but will only mark where each begins. The second

part begins 'Why do you weep . . .', the third 'Leave to us . . .', and the fourth: 'She reveals . . .'.

XXIII

A few days later I was struck down in a certain part of my body with a serious illness which caused me very severe pain. This made me so weak that I was forced to lie still like a paralysed man. Then on the ninth day, while undergoing unendurable pain, a thought came to me of my lady. And when I had reflected on her a little, my thoughts turned to my own frail life; realizing its small chances of lasting, even with good health, I wept at the misery of it all. Sighing deeply, I said within myself: 'One day the gentle Beatrice will be forced to die.'

At this I was overcome by such delirium that I shut my eyes and started to thrash about like a fever patient. My imagination at the beginning of its wanderings thrust before me the faces of ladies with their hair dishevelled. They said to me 'You too shall die.' Then after these ladies came more strange and terrifying faces, which said: 'You are dead.'

Owing to the vagaries of my imagination, I did not know where I was, and I thought I saw ladies wandering along a road, their hair tumbling down and sad beyond belief. Then I saw the sun darken and the stars changed to such a colour that I thought they wept; birds dropped dead while flying through the air, and there were vast earthquakes.[1] While I marvelled at this fantasy and was much frightened by it, I imagined a friend of mine came up and said: 'Have you not

1. This sick-bed vision and the canzone to which it gave rise act not only as a preparation for Beatrice's death but also as the only description of it we are given. The terrifying omens on a cosmic scale, the earthquakes, the darkening of the sun, and the weeping

heard? Your miraculous lady has left this world.' Then I began to weep sorrowfully, not only in my imagination but with my eyes, which were flowing with real tears.

Then I thought of looking towards heaven and I saw a flight of angels returning above and preceded by a small cloud of purest white. These angels were singing gloriously 'Hosanna in the Highest' and I seemed to hear nothing else. My heart, where Love lived in all his greatness, said to me: 'It is true that your lady is lying dead.' Then I seemed to go and behold the body which had once held the noblest and most blessed of souls. So strong was my wandering imagination that it showed me this lady lying dead; women were covering her with a white veil, while her face was clothed in such humility that she seemed to be saying: 'I behold the fount of peace.'

Seeing her, I felt myself become so humble that I called for Death and said: 'Kindest Death, come and do not spurn me. How gentle you must have become from visiting her! Come to me, for I want you above all else; you will see that I already wear your colours.' When I had witnessed all the mournful rites which are carried out on the bodies of the dead, I seemed to return to my own room, where I gazed in the direction of heaven. So strong was the force of my imagination that I began to weep and to say: 'O loveliest of souls, how blessed is the man who sees you.' While I uttered these words with sobs torn from the depths of my frame, and while I called on Death to come to me, a young girl[1] of great feeling, who was beside my bed, was so frightened that she

stars recall the darkness which lay over the earth at the time of the Crucifixion and so prepare for the full identification of Beatrice with Christ which comes in the fourteenth sonnet.

1. The young girl is said to have been Dante's sister.

began to weep herself, believing that my sobbing and moaning was caused by the pain of my illness. Whereupon some other ladies who were in the room noticed, because of the girl's crying, that I was weeping. This girl, who was a close relation of mine, they led away. Then, thinking that I was dreaming, they drew near to waken me and said: 'Sleep no more; take comfort.' As they were speaking, the powerful vision stopped, just at the point when I was about to say: 'O Beatrice, how blessed you are.' I had already said the words 'O Beatrice . . .' when I came to and opened my eyes and saw that I had been deceived; but although I had uttered that name, my voice was so broken with sobs that these ladies could not have understood me.

Although I was deeply disconcerted, warned by Love I turned towards them. When they saw me, they said: 'He seems to be dead.' And they said to one another: 'Let us try and comfort him.' While they were saying many things for my solace, they asked me what had terrified me. By that time, being somewhat restored and having recognized the insubstantiality of my dream, I answered: 'I will describe it all to you.' Then I related everything I had seen, from the beginning to the end, except that I withheld the name of my lady. Later, when I was cured of my illness, I intended to write something about what had happened, since it seemed intimately connected with my love, and so I wrote this canzone.

THE SECOND CANZONE

A girl as fresh and tender as her years
And endowed with human kindness,
Was present when I called for Death.

Seeing my eyes distraught with fears
  And hearing my empty words' distress,
  She wept from terror at my grief;
And other ladies who learned of my state
  From this girl's crying and dismay
  Led her away
  And attempted to restore
  My senses. 'Sleep no more,'
They said. 'Why are you so disconsolate?'
  Then the strange fantasy stopped its game
  Just when I uttered my lady's name.

So choked with suffering were my cries
  And broken with the anguish of weeping,
  I alone grasped the name in my heart
  And with that look which shame implies
  Which then held my face in its keeping,
I turned towards them, warned by Love's art;
So struck were they by my expression
  That their thoughts on Death all ran.
  'Let us console this man.'
  Then each begged with humility,
  And asked frequently:
'What did you see to cause this depression?'
  So when I felt restored once more,
  I said, 'I will tell you what I saw.'

While I was pondering my own frail life
  And saw how short a time it could last,
  Love in his home in my heart gave a cry;
  At this my soul was plunged in such strife
  That into my mind a thought then passed:
  'My lady will certainly die.'

Such delirium seized me at this
   That I closed my eyes, which were dully weighed,
   And so dismayed
Were my senses, they dispersed in flight.
Then in this dream of night,
   Far from all truth and consciousness,
   Tormented faces of women went by,
Saying, 'You will die, you will die.'

Then by this empty dream bedevilled
   I saw many things with certainty failing
   And did not know in what place I might be.
   Seeing women wander, their hair dishevelled,
   Some weeping loudly, others wailing
   Who shot flaming arrows in misery.
Then it seemed that by gradual course
   The sun darkened, and stars were peeping,
   Both of them weeping;
   Birds on the wing died in the air
   And the earth shook there,
   As a man appeared, discoloured and hoarse,
   Telling me: 'What! Has no one said?
Your beautiful lady is now dead.'

Raising my eyes, which were wet from crying,
   I saw like a rainfall of manna
   A flight of angels returning to heaven
   With a tiny cloud before them flying;
   After which all shouted 'Hosanna!' –
I would say if more had been given.
Then Love said: 'Nothing will be hidden.
   Come and see where your lady is lying.'

The false imagining
Conducted me to my lady's bed
And letting myself be led
I saw her shrouded with a veil by women;
And such humility did her face release
She seemed to be saying, 'I am in peace.'

I became so humbled in suffering
  Seeing in her such humility
  That I said: 'Death I cherish you more;
  You must have become a gentle thing
  Since you have visited my lady,
  And so should pity me and not withdraw.
  Realize I desire to become
  One of yours, and pledge you my all.
Come to my heart's call.'
Then I departed, devoured by this moan
  And when once alone
  I cried upwards to the highest kingdom:
  'Lovely soul, how blest is the man who sees you!'
You called me then, to please you.

This canzone has two parts; in the first, speaking to some one undefined, I describe how some ladies wakened me from an illusory dream and how I promised to tell it to them; in the second part I relate what I said to them. The second part begins 'While I was pondering . . .'. The first subdivides into two sections; in the first section I say how this girl and the ladies were affected by my dreaming before I returned to reality, while the second deals with what they said when I awoke from my delirium. The second section starts 'So choked with suffering . . .'. From 'While I was pondering . . .' onwards, I describe the dream; this also has two sections. In the first I relate the dream in its proper order, and in the second I secretly thank those who woke me up. The second section starts 'You called me then . . .'.

XXIV

AFTER this empty delusion, it happened that one day, while I was sitting thinking to myself, I felt a trembling begin in my heart, just as though I had been in the presence of my lady. Then I was overwhelmed by a vision of Love. He seemed to come from the direction of my lady, and, speaking in my heart with the greatest joy, he said: 'You should bless the day when I possessed you.' At this I could scarcely recognize my heart in its new condition, it was so joyful.

After my heart had told me these words in the language of Love, I saw approaching a lady famous for her beauty, who was the beloved of my greatest friend. Her real name was Giovanna,[1] but because of her beauty she had been given the name Primavera by some, and so she was known. While I watched, I saw come after her the miraculous Beatrice. These ladies walked close to me, and I heard Love say in my heart: 'She is called Primavera only because of her coming today, for I made the giver of the name call her that; Primavera, the Spring, or Prima verrà, she will come first on the day that Beatrice shall show herself as her followers imagine her. And her real name, Giovanna, can also be related to the first coming, since it derives from the John who preceded the true light, saying: 'I am the voice of one crying in the wilderness; prepare ye the way of the Lord.' He also seemed to

1. Giovanna was one of the several loves of Guido Cavalcanti. In this sonnet the identification of Christ with Beatrice is made clear even to the point of providing her with a John the Baptist.

say these words to me: 'If you wanted to think very subtly, Beatrice could be called Love, for she greatly resembles me.' Reflecting about this, I intended to write a poem to this friend of mine – keeping certain words back – as I believed his heart would wonder once more at the beauty of Primavera. So I wrote this sonnet.

THE FOURTEENTH SONNET

Within my heart I sensed awaken
  A loving spirit which slept
  And from a distance Love then stepped
So happy, I felt almost mistaken.

He said: 'Think only of extending my fame.'
  He laughed at each single word;
  Then standing still by my side, my lord
Gazed back at the way whence he came.

I saw Giovanna and my lady Beatrice
  Come up to where I was standing;
  One wonder after another in show.
And as my memory repeats it like this,
Love told me: 'The first is called Spring;
  The other's name is Love, she resembles me so.'

This sonnet has several parts; in the first of these I describe how I felt awaken in me the accustomed tremor and how Love in a state of happiness appeared in my heart from a great distance. The second part described what Love said to me in my heart, and how it struck me; the third deals with the things I heard and saw after he remained by my side for a while. The second part begins 'He said: "Think only ..."', the third 'Then standing still ...'. This last part subdivides into two: the first deals with what I saw, and the

second with what I heard. This second sub-section starts
'Love told me . . .'.

XXV

At this point[1] the more intelligent reader might be per-
plexed by my treatment of Love as a thing in itself, and not
merely an intelligent being, but also a bodily one. Strictly
speaking, this is false, since Love is a quality of a being but
does not exist as an individual being. That I speak of him as
having a body and as being a man, appears from three things
I say of him. I say that I saw him coming from a distance;
in this case, since *coming* implies motion in space – according
to Aristotle only a body is capable of spatial movement by
itself – it would appear that I state Love to be a body. I also

1. The last appearance of Love is in the fourteenth sonnet. After
pointing out the similarity between her and himself he vanishes, not
to appear again. In this long digression Dante first stresses that Love
is an accident – that is, in scholastic talk, an attribute of a substance –
and then goes on to give his authorities for personifying him. Just as
Love himself in the second vision said that the dissimulation or false
image must be done away with, so Dante breaks down the image of
Love to get closer to Beatrice, who contains that love.

If the reader finds this disgression somewhat tortured and the
reasoning odd, he should remember that by writing in Italian and not
in Latin, Dante was conscious of his temerity in breaking with the
ancient tradition of writing all serious works in the language of the
Church. Here he states that only matters dealing with Love should
be written in the vernacular, but as he grew older so his outlook on
this question broadened. Even after Dante's death, however, his
example was not enough to reassure Italian writers that it was legiti-
mate to write of serious matters in their own tongue. Petrarch believed
that his fame would live mostly through his Latin works, notably
his epic, *Africa*.

In justifying his use of metaphor and personification Dante quotes
from the classical poets much as a scholastic philosopher of his day
would bolster his arguments with quotations from the Church Fathers.

say of him that he laughs and smiles, both of which qualities are peculiar to man, especially laughter. Thus it would seem that I assume him to be a man.

To explain as much as is necessary here, it should first be understood that in ancient times there were no love poets in our common tongue, although there were certain love poets writing in Latin. I refer here to our own country, though it may have happened among other races, especially in Greece, that these matters were dealt with not by vernacular poets but by literary ones. It is only in recent years that poets have written in the vernacular; for to write rhyming verse in our own language is equivalent to writing Latin verse in metre. A sign of how recent this development must be is that if we were to search through Provençal and Italian literature we should find nothing composed earlier than one hundred and fifty years before the present time. The reason why some unskilled writers made such a reputation by their poetry is that they were about the first to write in Italian. The first man to write as a vernacular poet did so because he wished to make his meaning clear to a lady who had difficulty in understanding Latin. This is a warning to those who use rhyme for other subjects than those of Love, since from the beginning this method of composing was invented solely for speaking of Love.

As poets are allowed greater licence of speech than prose writers, and since writers of rhymed verse are simply poets in the vernacular, it is perfectly reasonable that they should be allowed greater licence than their fellow-writers in the vernacular. Continuing this argument, it can be seen that any figure of speech or rhetoric used by the Latin poets should be permitted to the present writers in rhyme. Therefore, if we find that the poets addressed inanimate objects as though they had sense and reason, and made them converse, using not only real things but invented things – that is to say that they have said that non-existent things and qualities of things speak as though their beings were men – the rhyming poet can do the same. This should not be done without reason, but with an intention which can be made clear later in prose. That poets have spoken in such a way appears in Virgil, who in the first book of the Aeneid makes Juno, a goddess hostile to the Trojans, speak thus to Aeolus, the lord of the winds: '*O Aeolus, for to you, etc.*' And Aeolus answers her: '*It is yours, O queen, to choose.*' In the third book of the Aeneid inanimate object speaks to animate, as in: '*O bold Trojans, etc.*' In Lucan the animate speaks to the inanimate: '*You owe much, O Rome, to civil arms.*' Horace addresses his own art directly, as though speaking to another man, not even using his own words but quoting those of great Homer, in his *Art of Poetry*: '*Tell me, Muse, of the Man, etc.*' In Ovid, Love speaks as though he were a human being, in the beginning of *The Remedy for Love*: '"*Wars, I see, wars are in store for me,*" *he said.*' This should clarify the difficulties to be found in this book.

To prevent any fool's taking advantage of this, I must make it plain that these poets did not speak thus without reason, nor should any modern poet use these figures of speech without basing them on some clear meaning. Any man would be disgraced if after filling his poems with metaphors and rhetorical figures he could not strip his work of these ornaments to reveal a true meaning, when asked to do so. My greatest friend and I are aware of several who write in this stupid manner.

XXVI

THAT most gentle lady who is spoken of in the preceding words came to be held in such esteem by people that when she passed along the street they would run after her to see her. I felt a miraculous joy at this. When she passed close to anyone, such modesty would awake in his heart that he would not dare to raise his eyes to reply to her greeting. Any one who does not believe this can find it substantiated by many men from their own experience. Crowned and clothed in humility, she would continue on her way, showing no vanity at what she saw and heard. After she had gone by, many would say: 'She is not a woman, but one of the loveliest angels in heaven.' Others would repeat: 'She is a wonder; blessed be God who can work such miracles.' She behaved so gently and with such grace that all who saw her experienced in themselves a warm and modest charm which they could never describe afterwards. No one could look at her without sighing deeply. These and even more remarkable things proceeded from her power. Reflecting on this and wishing to return to her praises, I determined to write something describing her miraculous and excellent works, not only for those who were able to see her with their own eyes, but so that others might know of her as much as can be conveyed in words. So I wrote this sonnet.

THE FIFTEENTH SONNET

Such gentleness and charm are shown
   In my lady's greeting to those who come
   That all tongues tremble and are dumb
And their eyes dare not meet her own.

Hearing her praises, she goes forth
   Benignly clothed in humbleness
   And seems to be the living witness
Of a miracle from heaven on earth.

She reveals such charm to a man nearby
  That his heart grows sweet at her sight
– Only the experienced can understand –

While from her face there seems to expand
  A calming spirit full of Love's light,
  Which says to the soul in moving: 'Sigh!'

This sonnet is plain enough to understand from what I have already said, so there is no need to divide it. So, leaving it,

XXVII

I SAY that my lady came to possess such grace that not only was she held in high honour and praise, but many others derived worth and esteem on her account. Seeing this and wishing to reveal it to those who had not realized it, I decided to write something in which this would be made clear. So I wrote the sonnet beginning 'Who sees my lady . . .', describing how her virtue influences others, as can be seen below.

THE SIXTEENTH SONNET

Who sees my lady with other women around
  Beholds the whole source of salvation,
  And those accompanying her must be bound
To thank God for his grace in creation.

So strong is her beauty in its stealth
  That others can feel no enviousness;
  Instead it makes them resemble herself
In love, in faith, and in gentleness.

The sight of her makes all things humble
  Showing not only her to be lovely
  But all who receive from her a due part;

And in her deeds she is so gentle
  That none can recall her to memory
  But Love sends a sigh from his heart.

This sonnet has three parts; the first says among what people this lady appeared to even greater advantage, the second deals with the graciousness of her company, and in the third I relate the extraordinary effect she had on others. The second part starts 'And those accompanying . . .', and the third 'So strong . . .'. This last part subdivides into three; the first of these describes her effect on other women – that is, on themselves. In the second part I say how they were able to influence others by what they gained from her; the third describes how it was not only over women that she had this power, but over everyone. This did not happen in her presence alone, but through the very memory of her The second part starts 'The sight . . .', and the third 'And in her deeds . . .'.

XXVIII

ONE day after this I began to reflect on what I had said about my lady in these two preceding sonnets. Realizing that I had not described her present effect on me, it struck me that I had not spoken fully enough. Therefore I intended to write something in which I would describe how absolutely open I seemed to be to her power, and how her great virtue worked in me. Since I did not consider I could contain all this in the short scope of a sonnet, I started a canzone, which began:

THE THIRD CANZONE

Love has possessed me for so long
  And made me familiar with his rule
  That just as at first he seemed cruel
Now in my heart his sweetness is strong.

So when my strength is bound by his capture
  And my senses seem to take flight,
  My weak soul feels such keen delight
That my face goes pale with rapture.

Then Love assumes such domination
  That he sends my sighs out speaking
  And forth they wander beseeching
My lady to grant me further salvation.

This befalls whenever she sees me
  And is so humble no one believes me.

XXIX

'How doth the city sit solitary, that was full of people! How is she become as a widow.'

I was just at the beginning of this canzone and had completed the part which has been given above, when the Lord of Justice called the gentlest of women to glory under the banner of the Blessed Virgin Mary, whose name had always been held in the greatest reverence in the speech of Beatrice the blest.

Although it would probably be interesting now if I described her parting from us, I do not intend to do so, for three reasons: the first is that it is not within the context of this book,[1] if we are to go by its prologue; the second is that even if it were within the present context, my pen is not yet capable of treating it as it deserves; the third is that even if the first two reasons could be passed over, it is not for me of all people to describe it, since I should be constrained to sing my own praises – which would be both tasteless and reprehensible. And so I will leave it for some other commentator.

However, the number nine[2] has often occurred in this book, and there is a great deal of reason for it, as it played a great part in her death. I ought to say something about it, since it seems to be to the point. First I will say what part it played in her departure, and give a reason why it was especially connected with her.

1. 'The first is that it is not within the context of this book': Both the first and the third of Dante's reasons for not describing Beatrice's death are very obscure. The second, that he is incapable of dealing with it as it deserves, is clear enough; but how Dante would be departing from his declared intention, as set out in the prologue, or how he would be forced to sing his own praises, few have professed to understand. There is an excellent discussion of the matter in Charles S. Singleton's *An Essay on the Vita Nuova* (Harvard University Press, 1949).

2. The number nine and the death of Beatrice. It has been calculated from this passage that Beatrice died within the hour after sunset on 8 June 1290. Each of the three visions foretelling the death of Beatrice is connected with the number nine, and here Dante steps aside from his main story to explain his previous many references to the number. He gives two reasons for the special significance of nine and Beatrice, the first connecting the birth of Beatrice with the most perfect conjunction of the heavens and therefore with the outer world, and the second with the inner nature of Beatrice. By a pun on the word '*nove*', which means both nine and a new thing or miracle, Dante shows that the creation of Beatrice was the work of the Trinity itself.

XXX

ACCORDING to the Arab calendar, her noble soul departed in the first hour of the ninth day of the month. According to the Syrian calendar, it departed in the ninth month of the year, because their first month is Tisrin I, which corresponds to our October. According to our calendar, it departed in the year of our era, that is of our Lord, which completed the perfect number (10) for the ninth time in the century in which she lived in this world. She was one of the Christians of the thirteenth century. A reason why this number was so especially attached to her might be that, according to Ptolemy and to Christian truth, there are nine heavens which move; since the common opinion of astrologers is that these heavens affect us here below according to their conjunctions, this number was her friend, because it explained that at her birth all the nine moving heavens were in their most perfect conjunction. That is one reason; but another is that if one thinks more subtly, and according to infallible truth, she herself was this number. I mean this as an analogy, and this is how I understand it: the number three is the root of nine, since it makes nine when multiplied by itself without any other number, just as we say three times three makes nine. Since three is the root of nine, and the sole root of miracles is three, the Father, the Son, and the Holy Ghost which are three and one, this lady was accompanied by the number nine so that it should be made clear that she was a new thing, that is a miracle, whose root was solely in the Trinity. A cleverer man might perhaps see an even more subtle reason for it, but this is what I see, and this pleases me most.

XXXI

AFTER this gentlest of women had left this world, our city remained as though widowed and despoiled of all dignity. I, still weeping in this desolate town, wrote to the Princes of the land about its condition, taking the opening of Jeremiah: 'How doth the city sit solitary!' I say this so that no one need wonder why I quoted it before as the gateway to the new matter which comes after. If some one wishes to complain of me for not reproducing here the words which followed this quotation, my excuse is that I did not intend to write here anything which was not in the common language; since the words following this quotation are all in Latin, I should be breaking my purpose if I were to write them down. Also, my friend to whom I am writing this intended that I should write to him only in the common tongue.

XXXII

AFTER my eyes had been weeping for some time, they were so exhausted I could no longer express my misery, and I thought I would ease it a little by writing a lament. I decided to make a canzone in which I would lament her whose loss had destroyed my soul. And so I began 'My eyes out of pity . . .'.

In order that this canzone should seem even more widowed at its ending, I will give its division here. I will keep to this method from here onwards. This miserable canzone has three parts, the first of which acts as an introduction; in the second part I speak of her, and in the third I speak to the poem itself. The second part begins 'Beatrice has gone . . .',

and the third 'My sad song . . .'. The first part subdivides
into three; in the first I explain what moved me to speak; in
the second I say for whom this poem is intended; and in the
third I say of whom I speak. The second sub-division starts
'And since I recall . . .', and the third 'While I now weep . . .'.
Then, when I say 'Beatrice has gone . . .', this has two sections. First I give the reason why she was taken from us and
then, in the part beginning 'Now it has abandoned . . .', I
describe how people mourned the loss of her. This last
section subdivides into three. In the first I name the man
who does not weep for her; in the second those who do
weep; and in the third I name my own condition. The second
subdivision starts 'But he has sadness and misery . . .', and
the third 'And anguish comes . . .'. Then, when I say 'My
sad song . . .', I address this canzone of mine, point out to
which ladies it should go, and say that it should remain
with them.

THE FOURTH CANZONE

My eyes out of pity for my heart
   Have endured such pain and grief,
   They can weep no more, from sheer exhaustion;
So if I wish to ease the great smart
Which slowly and surely leads me to Death,
   I am forced to utter my lamentation
   And since I recall I used to mention
Willingly to you, ladies of kindness,
My lady while she was living and near,
   I want none other to hear
   But the gentle hearts ladies possess.
While I now weep I shall speak of her,
Since she fled to heaven so suddenly,
   Leaving Love here to lament with me.

Beatrice has gone to the height of heaven,
  To the realm where the angels know peace;
  She stays with them, leaving you behind.
Neither by heat nor cold was she taken,[1]
Excess of which causes others' decease
  But only by her benignity of mind;
  For the light of her humbleness climbed
Into heaven with such power and direction
That the everlasting Lord was made to wonder
  And come under
  A sweet desire to summon such perfection.
Calling her, he made her sunder
Herself from this life which was so wearying
  It did not deserve such a gentle thing.

Now it has abandoned her lovely frame,
  Her gentle soul so full of grace
  Dwells in the glory it deserved to win.
Who does not mourn when he utters her name
Has a heart of rock so evil and base
  That a benign spirit cannot enter in.
  The brutish heart has no wit to imagine
A conception of all she presents
And thus it knows no desire to cry.
  But he has sadness and misery
  Of sighing, and a doom of laments,
With deprivation of all things consolatory,
Who even once recalls to his ken
  What she was and how she was taken.

1. 'Neither by heat nor cold was she taken': This refers to the old
medical doctrine of the four humours of the body, heat, cold, wet, and
dryness. An imperfect balance of these led to disease or death.

And anguish comes with my sigh's breath
  When my heavy memories entreat
  Her who has stricken my heart in two;
And frequently while thinking on Death
I am overcome by desire so sweet
  That my face's colour is changed to view.
  When the delusion has bound me too,
I am seized by such pain in my frame
That the suffering I feel restores me
  And then transforms me,
  That I am separated from men by shame.
Then I weep when loneliness draws me,
Calling on Beatrice: 'You are now dead!'
  And while I call her I am comforted.

  Tears of sorrow and sighs of anguish
Lay waste my heart when I am alone
Which would melt any men to hear;
  And how my heart has lost its flourish
  Since to the new time my lady has gone,
No tongue exists to relate its fear;
And even, ladies, if I had the desire,
  I could not describe myself to you,
  So trampled am I by bitter life
  Which has made such strife
That all men seem to say 'I abandon you'
Seeing my face where Death runs rife;
  But whatever I am, my lady can see
  And from her I still hope for mercy.

My sad song, go weeping on your way
And find those girls and women
  To whom your sisters were bidden
  And used to bring such gladness.

You, the daughter of sadness,
Must go comfortless to them.

XXXIII

AFTER this canzone had been set down, a man came to see me who might be considered my second-greatest friend. No one was more closely related to that citizen of Heaven than he. When he had spoken to me, he begged me to write something for him about a lady who had died; although he disguised his words so that they should seem to refer to another lady who had recently died, I realized that he actually meant the blessed Beatrice, and so I said I would carry out his wish. Reflecting on this, I decided to write a sonnet which would contain my lamentation and to give it to my friend so that it should appear to have been written for him. So I composed 'O gentle hearts'.

This sonnet has two parts; in the first I call on the faithful followers of Love to hear me; in the second I describe my miserable state. The second part begins 'Hear them . . .'.

THE SEVENTEENTH SONNET

O gentle hearts, come and follow
The course of my comfortless sighs;
Hear them for compassion cries;
Without them I would die of sorrow;

Because my eyes would suffer more
Than I could hope to repay
In weeping, alas! for my lady
To ease my heart's cruel sore.

You will hear them often lament
My gentle lady who has flown
To a world which fits her perfection,

And scorn this life which on its own
In the suffering soul's form and content
Is bereft of its true salvation.

XXXIV

When I had written this sonnet and had thought about the man for whom it was intended, it struck me that it was a totally insufficient service for someone so closely related to that glorious lady. So before I handed him this sonnet I wrote two stanzas of a canzone; one of these stanzas was in fact for him, but the other was for myself, although at a cursory glance they both seemed to be composed for one person. But anyone who inspects them closely will soon see that different people speak in them; for in the first the speaker does not call her 'his' lady, as is done in the second. I gave him the sonnet and the canzone, saying I had written them entirely for him.

The canzone begins 'How often, alas!' and has two parts; the first stanza contains the lament of my dear friend who was so closely related to her, in the second stanza, starting 'My sighs gather . . .', it is I who lament. So it can be seen in this canzone that two people mourn her, one as a brother and the other as a servant.

THE FIFTH CANZONE

How often, alas! have I remembered
That never again shall I
See the lady whom I mourn apart.

Such grief has my aching mind assembled
Within my heart,
I say: 'My soul, you should fly.'
For dread of tortures you will come by
In this world you already detest
  Makes me tremble with fear.
  So now I call Death here
  As my sweet and soothing rest.
Crying 'Come!' with so impassioned a sigh
I am jealous of all men who die.

My sighs gather their powers in one whole
For a sound of compassion
  To call on Death in every way.
  All my desires have him as their goal
Since my lady, I say,
Was struck in his cruel fashion;
And so the delight of her lovely perfection
On rising beyond our range of vision
  Became a great beauty of the spirit
  So that heaven is lit
  By a light of Love, giving the angels salutation;
And their intellect in all its subtleties
Wonders aloud: 'How gentle it is!'

XXXV

ON the first anniversary of the day when that lady was made
a citizen of eternal life, I was sitting down and was drawing
an angel on a tablet while I remembered her. While I drew I
turned my eyes and I saw that standing beside me were some
people whom I ought to welcome. They were looking at

what I was doing, and, according to what I was afterwards told, they had already been there some time before I realized it. When I saw them I rose and greeted them, saying: 'Some-one was with me just now and I was thinking about that.' When they had gone, I returned to my work of drawing the faces of angels. While I was doing this, I thought of writing a poem for her anniversary and of addressing it to my visitors. So I wrote this sonnet, which begins 'To my mind . . .'. This has two beginnings, and so I will divide it according to each.

According to the first beginning this sonnet has three parts; in the first I say that this lady was already in my memory, the second describes Love's effect on me because of this, and the third tells of the consequences. The second part begins 'Love who had felt her . . .', and the third 'Weeping they issue . . .'. This last part has two sub-divisions; in the first of these I say that these sighs spoke as they issued, while the second describes how some sighs uttered words which differed from the rest. This second subdivision starts 'But those . . .'. The second version can be divided in the same way, except that in the variant quatrain I give the occasion when I remembered that lady, which I do not do in the first version.

THE EIGHTEENTH SONNET

FIRST BEGINNING

To my mind memory restored
The gentle lady who for her quality
Was placed in the heaven of humility
Where Mary is, by the most high Lord.

SECOND BEGINNING

To my mind memory restored
*   That gentle lady whom Love laments*
*   Just at the time when her power intense,*
To see how I did, drew you abroad.

Love who had felt her in my mind
*   Awoke in my heart's great waste*
*   And told my sighs: 'Go out in haste.'*
So they went wailing in their kind.

Weeping they issue from my breast
*   With a single voice, and often drain*
*   Dolorous tears from my sad eyes;*

But those which cause the keenest pain
*   Come crying out: 'O mind of the blest,*
*   A year has passed since you rose to the skies.'*

XXXVI

A LITTLE time later, while I was in a place remembering past time, I was standing deep in thought and obsessed with painful reflections which gave my face an expression of utter bewilderment. Realizing my condition, I looked around to see if anyone had been watching me. Then I saw a young and lovely lady who was gazing at me out of a window[1] with such pity that all compassion seemed to be contained in her face. At this – just as unhappy people, seeing others' sympathy for them, are more quickly made to weep as though

1. The first appearance of the lady of the window. Many attempts have been made to identify this lady with a Florentine lady of the time, but none successfully.

they had compassion on themselves – so I felt my eyes brimming with tears. Not wanting to reveal my wretched life, I departed from the sight of this compassionate woman, and then said to myself: 'Noble Love must certainly be with this lady.' So I decided to write a sonnet in which I would speak to her and in which I would include everything which has been told here. Since this is clear enough, I will not divide it. The sonnet begins 'My eyes beheld . . .'.

THE NINETEENTH SONNET

My eyes beheld the great sympathy
  Which had appeared in your face
When you understood my desperate case
Which bewildered me with misery.

Then I saw that you had surmise
  How dark was the nature of my life,
  So that fear coursed my heart in strife
Lest disgrace was revealed in my eyes.

So I turned away; the tears seeping
  I felt spring up in my breast
  Which had been moved by the sight of you.

I spoke then to my sad soul anew:
  'With this lady the same Love must rest
  Who makes me wander thus weeping.'

XXXVII

WHENEVER this lady saw me her face grew pale and pitying as though she were in love; this often reminded me of my departed lady, who used to look at me in a similar way. Many times, certainly, not being able to weep or express my sadness, I went to see this lady, whose very aspect of compassion seemed capable of drawing the tears from my eyes. Thus the desire came on me to write something addressed to her, and so I composed this sonnet, 'Pallor of Love . . .'. It is plain enough, from what goes before it, to understand without any division.

THE TWENTIETH SONNET

Pallor of Love and open compassion
    Have never before so helped to soften
    A woman's face from beholding often
Eyes of gentleness and tears of passion,

As they did yours when as you were looking
    You saw my features in misery confined,
    So that from you such thoughts came to mind
I have fears my heart may be breaking.

I cannot hold my shattered eyes back
    From gazing frequently on you,
    So greatly do they desire to cry;

You arouse that purpose they lack,
    So they are eaten with longing anew –
    But they cannot weep with you by.

XXXVIII

THIS lady began to have such an effect on me that my eyes enjoyed beholding her rather too greatly. I was often tortured by my emotions at this and thought myself vile. Many times I cursed the fickleness of my eyes and said to them: 'You used to make others weep who saw your sorrowful condition, but now it seems you want to forget it all because of this lady who watches you. She only watches because she is equally weighed down by the loss of the glorious lady for whom you used to mourn. Do what you can do, for I will often bring her memory back to you, accursed eyes, for your tears should never stop flowing till after death.' When I had spoken to my eyes in this manner, I was overwhelmed by great sighs and anguish. In order that this internal battle should not be known only to the miserable creature who endured it, I decided to write a sonnet, describing this appalling condition in it, and so I wrote the poem beginning 'That bitter weeping . . .'.

This sonnet has two parts; in the first I speak to my eyes, just as my heart spoke within me, while in the second part I remove any difficulties by making clear who it is that speaks. The second part begins 'So speaks . . .'. Perhaps more divisions might be made, but these would be superfluous since it is made understandable by what has already been said.

THE TWENTY-FIRST SONNET

That bitter weeping which you have shown
  So long a time, my eyes, once could wake
  Other men's compassion and would make
Everyone weep, as well you have known.

Now it seems that you would forget her
  If for my part I became so evil
  As not to resist your every cavil,
Recalling her whom you mourned together.

Your fickleness has given me dread
  And caused me strongly to waver
  At the sight of a lady who gazes in sorrow;

For except for death you should never
Forget our own lady who lies dead:
So speaks my heart, with a sigh to follow.

XXXIX

THE sight of this lady affected me so strangely that I was often deeply infatuated with her. I would think of her thus: 'She is young, beautiful, and intelligent and has perhaps appeared by the design of Love, so that my life may be comforted.' Frequently I fell deeper into this infatuation, so that my heart agreed to its reasoning. When it had consented to this, I reflected once more, as though moved by reason, and said to myself: 'What is this thought which attempts to console me in so depraved a disguise and will not let me think of anything else?' Then another thought rose up and said: 'Now you have known this suffering, why do you want to escape from its bitterness? You can see that this is an inspiration, which brings us the desires of Love and which arises from a source as charming as the eyes of this lady who has shown you such sympathy.' When I had undergone much conflict over this, I decided to write something about it. Since those which took her side won the battle of thoughts, I thought I should speak to her. So I wrote this sonnet, which begins 'A gentle thought . . .'. I say 'gentle' because it was addressed to a gentle lady, but otherwise it is absolutely unworthy.

In this sonnet I talk with two voices, just as my thoughts were divided into two camps. One of these is called the heart, or the appetite, and the other the soul, or reason; and I say what they said to one another. It should be clear enough to those whom I want to understand why the appetite should be called the heart and reason the soul. It is true that in the preceding sonnet I take the part of the heart against the eyes, and that this seems the reverse of what I am doing here. In that case I also meant the heart to be the appetite because then I still had a greater desire to remind myself of Beatrice rather than of this lady, even though it was only a little. From this it will be clear that there is no contradiction.

This sonnet has three parts; in the first I start by saying to this lady that all my desires have turned to her; in the second I tell how the soul or reason spoke to the heart or appetite; in the third part I give its answer. The second part starts 'The soul says . . .' and the third 'He answers her . . .'.

THE TWENTY-SECOND SONNET

A gentle thought which speaks of you
  Has often come to dwell with me
  And it talks of Love so charmingly
That my heart has consented thereto.

The soul says to the heart: 'Who has thus
  Come to console our intelligence?
  His power is so strong and intense
That no other thoughts may remain with us.'

He answers her: 'O thoughtful soul,
  This is Love in a new apparition
  Who offers his desires to my sense.
His life and the whole of his strong condition
Sprang from the eyes of this pitying girl
  Who was so disturbed by our torments.'

XL

In opposition to this enemy of reason, there arose within me one day at about midday a mighty vision. I beheld Beatrice in glory, clothed in that crimson dress in which she had first appeared to my eyes and seeming as young as when we first met. Then I began to think of her, and while I remembered her in the order of time's passing, my heart began to repent with great pain of the desire which had so basely possessed it in spite of the constancy of reason. Now that this evil desire had been expelled, all my thoughts turned back to my gentlest Beatrice. From then onwards I began to think of her with such shame in my heart that my sighs often made this clear, since nearly all spoke on their passage what was being said in my heart: the name of that gentlest of women and how she had departed from us. Frequently some thought would bring such suffering with it that I would forget both the thought and where I was.

From this rekindling of sighs, my relieved tears broke out again so much that my eyes seemed just two things whose only object was to weep. After crying for a long time, purple rings would appear around them as happens to a man who has been tortured. From this it appeared that their inconstancy was fittingly rewarded, for from that time they could not meet the gaze of anyone who looked at them with the intention of drawing them into the same trap. Wishing that such an evil desire and empty temptation should seem utterly destroyed, and that no poem of mine written before should be open to misinterpretation, I decided to write a sonnet in which I would include everything I have said here. So I wrote 'Alas! Because . . .'. I said 'Alas' because I was so ashamed of my wandering eyes. I will not divide this sonnet, because its purpose is plain enough.

THE TWENTY-THIRD SONNET

Alas! Because of the force of many sighs
Which are born of thoughts in my heart,
My conquered eyes have lost the art
Of returning the gaze of other men's eyes.

They are so made they have two desires
– To shed tears and show pain thereof –
And so often do they weep that Love
Rings them round with a crown of martyrs.

These thoughts and the sighs I carry
Within my heart are so choking
That Love pales with grief at each breath,
Because these sorrowing ones are invoking
The sweet name of my lady
And are inscribed with words on her death.

XLI

AFTER this tribulation, something happened at the time when many people go to see the blessed image[1] which Jesus Christ left us as an example of his beautiful countenance – that countenance at which even now my lady gazes in

1. 'The blessed image': This is the handkerchief of St Veronica, on which the face of Christ was imprinted. There is a subtle analogy between the journey of the pilgrims to see the true face of Christ and the stage which Dante had reached in his understanding of Love. He himself had just received a vision of Beatrice as she was when she first appeared to him, and this again emphasizes the Christlike nature of Beatrice.

glory. Some of these people were passing along a street which runs nearly through the middle of this city where that gentlest of women was born, lived, and died. These pilgrims were walking, it seemed to me, in a very reflective manner. Thinking of them, I said to myself: 'These pilgrims seem to come from a distant country, and I do not believe they could have heard of that lady. They would know nothing of her, and thus their thoughts must be of other things than those of the people here. Perhaps they are thinking of their far-off friends, whom we do not know.' Then I said to myself: 'I know that if they came from a near-by district they would seem outwardly distressed at passing through the middle of this mournful city.' Then I said to myself: 'If I could detain them a little I would make them weep as well before they left this city, because I would say words which would make any weep who heard them.' So when they had passed out of my sight I proposed to write a sonnet containing what I had said to myself. To make it even more appealing, I decided to write it as though I had spoken to them. The sonnet begins 'O pilgrims . . .'.

I said pilgrims according to the general use of the term, for 'pilgrims' may be understood in a broad and a narrow sense. In the former case, any one is a pilgrim who is outside his fatherland; in the narrow sense only the man who travels to or from the sanctuary of St James of Compostella. It should be known that there are three names for people who travel for the worship of God. Palmers are those who go to the Holy Land, from which they bring back palm branches; pilgrims are those who go to the sanctuary of Galicia, because the tomb of St James was further from his own country than that of any other apostle; *romei* are those who go to Rome, which is where these people I call pilgrims were going.

I will not divide this sonnet, because it should be clear enough.

THE TWENTY-FOURTH SONNET

> O pilgrims who wander and reflect
>   On something, perhaps in a distant place,
>   Do you spring from as far-off a race
> As might be thought from your aspect?
>
> For you do not weep when you pick your way
>   Through the midst of the city of sorrow,
>   Even like people who cannot follow
> The cause of her grave dismay.
>
> If you stay to hear the full story
>   My heart tells me truly in sighs
>   That away in tears you will creep:
> The city has lost her Beatrice,
>   And the words which describe her glory
>   Have the power to make other men weep.

XLII

THEN two ladies sent a request to me that I should send them some of my verses. So, having a great esteem for them, I intended to send some to them, together with a new poem written especially as a token of my regard for them. Thus I wrote a sonnet describing my condition and sent it with the preceding sonnet and one called 'Come and hear . . .'. The sonnet which I wrote them was 'A sigh from my heart . . .'.

This sonnet has five parts; in the first I say where my thought goes, giving the place the name of one of its effects. In the second I say why it goes upward, or in fact who draws it up. In the third I say what it saw: a lady receiving the honour due to her. It is called a 'pilgrim spirit' because in a spiritual sense it has left its fatherland. The fourth tells how it saw her state of glory, which was beyond my comprehension, for my thought rose so far into her being that my intellect could not understand it; for our intellect stands in the same relation to these blessed souls as our weak eyes to the sun. This is what Aristotle says in the second book of his Metaphysics. In the fifth part I say that although I cannot look into that region of her miraculous being where my thought draws me, I at least understand that this thought is entirely of my lady, because in it I often hear the name repeated. This fifth part concludes with 'dear ladies', so it should be understood that I am speaking to ladies. The second part begins 'The new intelligence . . .', the third 'When it has reached . . .', the fourth 'I cannot grasp . . .', and the fifth 'I know it describes . . .'. This sonnet could be made more intelligible by even further analysis, but I will leave it at that and will not bother to divide it any further.

THE TWENTY-FIFTH SONNET

A sigh from my heart flies above
  The farthest circling sphere of heaven:
  The new intelligence has been given
To draw it up, by weeping Love.

When it has reached its aim of desire
  It seems a lady receiving honour
  Who shines so that before her splendour
The pilgrim spirit must gaze and aspire.

I cannot grasp all its subtleties
When my sorrowing heart makes it tell
  Of this vision which it has scanned.

I know it describes this gentle marvel
For it often remembers Beatrice;
Then, dear ladies, I can understand.

XLIII

AFTER this sonnet a miraculous vision appeared to me, in which I beheld things which made me determine never to speak of that blessed lady until I could write worthily of her. To attain this end I study as hard as I can, as she knows in all truth. Therefore if it pleases Him through whom all things live that my life may continue for a few years, I hope to write of her what has never been said of any woman.

Then may it please God who is the Lord of Grace that my soul may rise to see the glory of its lady, who gazes in rapture on the face of Him 'who is blessed throughout all ages'.

A list of the most recent Penguin Classics
may be found overleaf

For a complete list of books available please write to Penguin Books whose address can be found on the back of the title page